Pharmacology
for Technicians

Fifth Edition

Workbook

Don A. Ballington • Mary M. Laughlin

Managing Editor:	Brenda M. Palo
Developmental Editor:	Grant E. Mabie
Production Editor:	Sarah Kearin
Cover and Text Designer:	Jaana Bykonich
Design and Production Specialists:	Valerie King and Timothy W. Larson

Care has been taken to verify the accuracy of information presented in this book. However, the authors, editors, and publisher cannot accept responsibility for Web, e-mail, newsgroup, or chat room subject matter or content, or for consequences from application of the information in this book, and make no warrantym, expressed or implied, with respect to its content.

Trademarks: Some of the product names and company names included in this book have been used for identification purposes only and may be trademarks or registered trade names of their respective manufacturers and sellers. The authors, editors, and publisher disclaim any affiliation, association, or connection with, or sponsorship or endorsement by, such owners.

Credits: Cover Images (top left) © iStockphoto/svengine svengine; (bottom left) ©iStockphoto/kzenon; (right) © iStockphoto/galdzer; page 79, Upsher Smith.

We have made every effort to trace the ownership of all copyrighted material and to secure permission from copyright holders. In the event of any question arising as to the use of any material, we will be pleased to make the necessary corrections in future printings. Thanks are due to the aforementioned authors, publishers, and agents for permission to use the materials indicated.

ISBN 978-0-76385-229-0

Contents

Preface

This workbook has been prepared to accompany the text *Pharmacology for Technicians, Fifth Edition* by Don A. Ballington and Mary M. Laughlin. Used in conjunction with the textbook and its Study Partner CD, this workbook reinforces student learning of drug groups, drug uses and effects, and other drug facts essential to the work of pharmacy technicians.

Correlated with the structure of the textbook, the workbook provides exercises for each of the 17 chapters, which are organized into four units. Instructors may choose to assign all or some of these exercises as homework or as take-home exams. Alternatively, students may use these exercises as an independent method of assessing their comprehension of the content discussed in the *Pharmacology for Technicians* textbook.

Overview of Chapter Exercises and Activities

Workbook exercises for Chapters 1 through 3 focus on the important foundation material presented in Unit 1, specifically the science of pharmacology and the study of pharmacokinetics.

Workbook exercises for the chapters of Units 2, 3, and 4 (Chapters 4–17) include a range of exercises requiring the recall of key information as well as the application of knowledge and critical thinking necessary in the pharmacy workplace. The following exercise types are provided for Chapters 4–17:

- *Reading Drug Labels and Medication Orders* requires students to apply literacy skills and drug-dispensing knowledge.

- *Understanding the Larger Medical Context* asks students to focus on medical issues such as disease states, anatomy and physiology, and drug classes in order to demonstrate an understanding of why certain drugs are prescribed, how they are used, and their pharmacokinetic effects.

- *Dispensing and Storing Drugs* asks students to identify storage requirements and auxiliary labels necessary to ensure patient safety and compliance.

- *Putting Safety First* expands on safety issues emphasized in the text by asking students to compare presented doses with standard or typical doses in order to recognize potential errors as well as to identify potential drug interactions.

- *Understanding Concepts* encourages students to explore drug classifications, types of medications and their applicability to disease states, and other issues critical to the work of a pharmacy technician.

All workbook chapters also contain one or more sets of matching questions that help students build their vocabulary related to the field of pharmacology.

Acknowledgments

The authors and editorial team at Paradigm Publishing, Inc. would like to thank Michelle C. McCranie, CPhT, of Ogeechee Technical College, Statesboro, GA, for her contribution in developing this workbook.

Comments and Questions

As an educational publisher, we are eager to provide the best possible textbook and supplements package for students and instructors. Your feedback can help us achieve that goal. Please reach us by clicking the "Contact Us" button on the home page of our company website at www.emcp.com.

Unit

1

Introduction to Pharmacology

Evolution of Medicinal Drugs

Understanding Pharmacology and Pharmacokinetics

1. A company plans to market a new antiseptic solution that prevents the spread of disease on hands and surgical equipment. The marketing department wants to name the product based on a pioneer in the field of chemical sterilization. What two pioneers would you choose? Explain your answer.

   _____

   _____

   _____

2. You are applying for a pharmacy technician job at a retail pharmacy in another state. In the job description, you note the following tasks:
   a. transferring prescriptions
   b. demonstrating to patients with asthma how to use a metered dose inhaler
   c. preparing prescription labels
   d. maintaining allergy information in the pharmacy system
   e. counseling diabetics with regard to insulin use

   Which of these requirements should not be part of the job description?

   _____

   _____

3. What was the first national pharmacy technician association?

   _____

4. Who organized PTEC, what was the purpose, and who published the first pharmacology textbook for technicians?

   _____

   _____

5. Put these groups related to pharmaceutical practice in order according to the year of their creation, starting with the earliest.

APhA   USP

FDA   DEA

_____

6. You are reading a newspaper ad about a drug named BPPA469 for the treatment of osteoarthritis. The ad states that healthy adults ages 18 to 45 years are to come in once a week to be examined while on BPPA469. What phase of a clinical trial do you think BPPA469 is in? Explain.

_____

_____

7. Which journal is the official publication for PTEC?

_____

8. If you were a student of Galen, what would you consider to be the source of disease?

_____

9. Name two drug classes that require medication guides to be given to patients at the time they pick up their prescriptions.

_____

10. Is a vaccine considered a therapeutic or a prophylactic drug? Explain.

_____

_____

11. During phase II of a clinical trial, patients are randomized to take either an active drug or a(n) _____ .

12. Methotrexate should never be used by pregnant women because of demonstrated harm to the fetus. This drug is in FDA Pregnancy Category _____ .

13. A good source for determining whether a generic drug is interchangeable with a brand name drug is the _____ .

14. To be made available without a prescription, a legend drug must have its status changed to _____ .

15. Pharmacy technicians must be recertified every _____ years by the PTCB.

16. The use of _____ drugs helps to keep the overall cost of healthcare down.

17. Problems with OTC products should be reported to the FDA's _____ or the ISMP.

18. Valerius Cordis published the _____ in 1546.

19. The *Pharmacopoeia of the United States* was published by the _____ .

20. Metoprolol tartrate and metoprolol succinate are examples of the same chemical that are available as two different _____ .

21. Homeopathic remedies use _____ doses of drugs.

22. Each drug seeking marketing status in the United States must have submitted and received an approved _____ .

23. Title II of the Comprehensive Drug Abuse Prevention and Control Act of 1970 designated five schedules for _____ according to the abuse probability of the drugs.

24. Insulin was first isolated by _____ .

25. In a(n) _____ study, neither trial participants nor research staff know which subjects are in the experimental group and which subjects are in the control group.

Matching–Terms and Definitions

_____ 26. A name that identifies a drug independently of its manufacturer; sometimes denotes a drug that is not protected by a trademark; also referred to as a USAN (United States Adopted Name)

_____ 27. A government grant that gives a drug company the exclusive right to manufacture a drug for a certain number of years; protects the company's investment in developing the drug

_____ 28. The agency of the federal government that is responsible for ensuring the safety of drugs and food prepared for the market

_____ 29. The entity, usually a pharmaceutical company, responsible for testing the efficacy and safety of a drug and proposing the drug for approval

_____ 30. The branch of the U.S. Justice Department that is responsible for regulating the sale and use of specified drugs, especially controlled substances

_____ 31. A medicinal substance or remedy used to change the way a living organism functions; also called a medication

_____ 32. A clinical trial in which neither the trial participants nor the study staff know whether a particular participant is in the control group or the experimental group

a. Black Box warning
b. brand name
c. C-I
d. C-II
e. C-III and C-IV
f. C-V
g. controlled substance
h. double blind study
j. drug
k. DEA
l. drug sponsor
m. FDA
n. generic name
o. homeopathy
p. legend drug
q. medication guide
r. OTC
s. patent
t. pharmacist
u. pharmacognosy
v. pharmacology
w. pharmacy technician
x. placebo
y. prophylactic drug
z. PTCB

_____ 33. A drug with potential for abuse; organized into five categories or schedules that specify whether and how the drug may be dispensed

_____ 34. A drug with the highest potential for abuse, which may be used only for research under a special license

_____ 35. A drug with a high potential for abuse, for which dispensing is severely restricted and prescriptions may not be refilled

_____ 36. A drug with a moderate potential for abuse, which can be refilled no more than five times in six months and only if authorized by the physician for this time period

_____ 37. A drug with a slight potential for abuse; some of which may be sold without a prescription depending on state law, but the purchaser must sign for the drug and show identification

_____ 38. A drug that may be sold only by prescription and must be labeled "Caution: Federal law prohibits dispensing without prescription" or "Rx only"

_____ 39. Specific information about certain types of drugs that is required by the FDA to be made available to the patient

_____ 40. A drug that may be sold without a prescription

_____ 41. One who is licensed to prepare and sell or dispense drugs and compounds and to fill prescriptions

_____ 42. A drug that prevents or decreases the severity of a disease

_____ 43. An inactive substance with no treatment value

national organization that develops
·macy technician standards and
·s a credentialing agency for
technicians

_____ 45. An individual working in a pharmacy who, under the supervision of a licensed pharmacist, assists in activities not requiring the professional judgment of a pharmacist

_____ 46. The study and identification of natural sources of drugs

_____ 47. The science of drugs and their interactions with the systems of living animals

_____ 48. Information printed on a drug package to alert prescribers to potential problems with the drug

_____ 49. The name under which the manufacturer markets a drug; also known as the trade name

_____ 50. A system of therapeutics in which diseases are treated by administering minute doses of drugs that, in healthy patients, are capable of producing symptoms like those of the disease being treated

Puzzling the Technician–Terms and Definitions

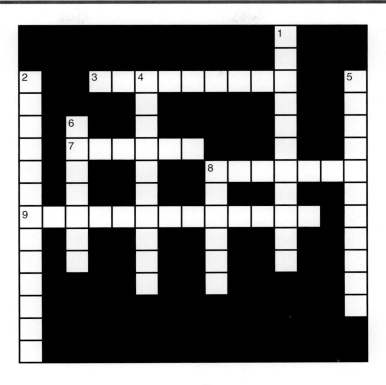

Across

3. Greek word meaning "magic spell"

7. American Civil War-era physician who first introduced antiseptics into surgery

8. an inactive substance given during drug trials

9. the monitored testing of drugs on humans (two words)

Down

1. a way to refer to a drug independent of manufacturer (two words)

2. an official listing of medicinal preparations

4. an older name for a pharmacist or pharmacy

5. ancient Greek who proposed that disease was caused by natural phenomena

6. discoverer of penicillin

8. a government grant that gives a company the exclusive right to manufacture a product for a certain number of years

Basic Concepts of Pharmacology

2

Understanding Pharmacology and Pharmacokinetics

1. Heart rate increases when beta-1 receptors are stimulated. A drug taken by a patient binds to the beta receptors. As a result, the patient's heart rate increases. Was the drug an antagonist or an agonist? Explain your answer.

   _____

   _____

2. What is the goal of drug therapy?

   _____

   _____

3. Why does the body act to maintain homeostasis?

   _____

4. Ciclopirox (Penlac) is an antifungal used to treat onychomycosis, a type of nail fungus. The directions say to apply the lacquer to each affected nail daily. Will the ciclopirox have a local or systemic effect? Explain your answer.

   _____

5. For many cases of infective endocarditis, the combination of gentamicin and ampicillin has been shown to be more effective than using each drug individually. The combination also allows the patient to avoid toxicities associated with the higher doses of gentamicin needed for separate dosing. How would you categorize the relationship of gentamicin and ampicillin when used together?

   _____

6. What are the two types of drug inhibition, and how do they differ?

   _____

   _____

7. Mrs. Holly, a patient with cancer, has been on high doses of Oxycontin for six months for pain. Her medication is being managed by an oncologist. Mrs. Holly does not experience euphoria when taking the prescribed dosage. Is she dependent on or addicted to Oxycontin? Explain your answer.

   _____

   _____

8. When a Z-pak is dispensed, the patient is told to take two tablets on the first day, and then one a day until all tablets are gone. What is the purpose of this dosage instruction, and what name is given to the first two tablets?

   _____

   _____

9. You read in a medical journal about a patient who developed an enlarged liver after taking a drug that has been available for 15 years. Although the enlarged liver can definitely be attributed to the drug, no such reaction has previously been reported. Is the response in this case allergic, anaphylactic, or idiosyncratic?

   _____

10. Drug A and drug B are both anticholinergics. To have equal effects, drug A must be dosed six times a day, while drug B is dosed two times a day. Which drug has the longer duration of action? Explain your answer.

   _____

   _____

11. What is half-life? How many half-lives are needed to eliminate a drug from the body?

   _____

   _____

12. The _____ prevents many drugs from penetrating the brain.

13. Vancomycin is usually dosed every 12 hours. If a dose was administered at 10:00 a.m., and the concentration of the drug in the blood had fallen to its lowest level at 9:30 p.m., that level would be considered a(n) _____ .

14. General anesthetics are excreted by the kidney, liver, and respiratory system. The sum excretion of all these systems is known as total body _____ .

15. Many geriatric patients experience a condition called gastroparesis, which greatly delays gastric emptying time. You would expect that this condition would also delay drug _____ .

16. Patients with impaired liver function who take drugs that are not excreted by the kidneys might expect drugs to be present for a _____ amount of time in the blood compared to patients with normal liver function.

17. Drugs that undergo extensive first-pass effect will have a lower _____ than those that do not.

18. Digoxin levels should be between 0.8 ng/mL and 2 ng/mL. A reading between those two numbers is considered to be in the _____ .

19. A drug has a blood plasma concentration of 20 mcg/mL. Ten hours later, the plasma concentration is 5 mcg/mL. This drug has a half-life of _____ hours.

Matching–Terms and Definitions

_____ 20. The strength by which a particular chemical messenger binds to its receptor site on a cell

_____ 21. A severe allergic response resulting in immediate life-threatening respiratory distress, usually followed by vascular collapse and shock and accompanied by hives

_____ 22. Drugs that bind to a receptor site and block the action of the endogenous messenger or other drugs

_____ 23. A specific molecule that stimulates an immune response

_____ 24. The process whereby a drug increases the concentration of certain enzymes that affect the pharmacologic response to another drug

_____ 25. The process whereby a drug blocks enzyme activity and impairs the metabolism of another drug

_____ 26. A change in the action of a drug caused by another drug, a food, or another substance such as alcohol or nicotine

_____ 27. Mathematical relationship between the blood concentration attained and the amount of drug administered

_____ 28. The degree to which a drug or other substance becomes available to the target tissue after administration

_____ 29. The time necessary for the body to eliminate half of the drug in the body at any time; written as $T_{1/2}$

_____ 30. Itching sensation

_____ 31. A barrier that prevents many substances from entering the cerebrospinal fluid from the blood; formed by glial cells that envelope the capillaries in the central nervous system, presenting a barrier to many water-soluble compounds though they are permeable to lipid-soluble substances

a. absorption

b. affinity

c. agonist

d. anaphylactic reaction

e. antagonist

f. antigen

g. bioavailability

h. blood-brain barrier

i. ceiling effect

j. dependence

k. distribution

l. elimination

m. first-pass effect

n. half-life

o. induction

p. inhibition

q. interaction

r. lipid

s. loading dose

t. local effect

u. maintenance dose

v. metabolism

w. pharmacokinetics

x. prophylaxis

y. pruritus

z. receptor

aa. solubility

bb. systemic effect

cc. therapeutic range

dd. trough

ee. volume of distribution

_____ 32. The extent to which the drug is metabolized by the liver before reaching systemic circulation

_____ 33. A fatty molecule, an important constituent of cell membranes

_____ 34. An action of a drug that is confined to a specific part of the body

_____ 35. Amount of a drug that will bring the blood concentration rapidly to a therapeutic level

_____ 36. Amount of a drug administered at regular intervals to keep the blood concentration at a therapeutic level

_____ 37. A point at which no chemical response occurs with increased dosage

_____ 38. The process by which drugs are chemically converted to other compounds

_____ 39. The activity of a drug within the body over a period of time; includes absorption, distribution, metabolism, and elimination

_____ 40. The process by which a drug moves from the blood into other body fluids and tissues and ultimately to its sites of action

_____ 41. A drug's ability to dissolve in body fluids

_____ 42. A state in which a person's body has adapted physiologically and psychologically to a drug and cannot function without it

_____ 43. The process whereby a drug enters the circulatory system

_____ 44. Removal of a drug or its metabolites from the body by excretion

_____ 45. The optimum dosage, providing the best chance for successful therapy

_____ 46. An action of a drug that has a generalized, all-inclusive effect on the body

_____ 47. Drugs that bind to a particular receptor site and trigger the cell's response in a manner similar to the action of the body's own chemical messenger

_____ 48. The lowest level of a drug in the blood

_____ 49. Effect of a drug in preventing infection or disease

Puzzling the Technician–Terms and Definitions

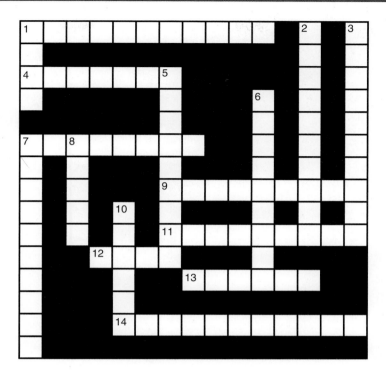

Across

1. use of a drug for disease prevention
4. a drug that produces a response similar to a natural chemical messenger
7. substance that produces an allergic response
9. dependence on a drug
11. the rate at which a drug is eliminated
12. the quantity of administration of a drug
13. elevated, red portions of the skin
14. state of biochemical stability of an organism

Down

1. the upper limit of the concentration of a drug
2. a symptom or condition for which a drug is known to be beneficial
3. physiological or psychological state in which one cannot function without a drug
5. decrease in response to continued administration of a drug
6. hives
7. a drug that binds to a receptor site and blocks action of a natural chemical messenger
8. important molecular constituent of cell walls
10. lowest concentration of a drug in the blood

Dispensing Medications

Understanding Pharmacology and Pharmacokinetics

1. How can a patient achieve relief with sublingual nitroglycerin when the oral route typically has an absorption phase of 15 to 30 minutes?

   _____

   _____

2. What two age groups require special attention when dispensing drugs? Explain your answer.

   _____

   _____

3. If a patient is vomiting and IV antiemetics are not available, what other route could be considered?

   _____

4. Why should technicians always check the dates on prescriptions?

   _____

   _____

5. If a prescriber wrote a prescription on 12-10-14 and the patient brings it in on 12-12-15, can it be filled?

   _____

6. What must be in place if someone comes into the pharmacy to get a flu shot? (Remember, the patient does not require a prescription.)

   _____

7. What are the advantages of administering a drug rectally?

   _____

   _____

8. List five drugs that are on both the Beers and Canadian lists to be avoided in the elderly.

     _____

     _____

9. The _____ is the part of a prescription that tells the patient how to take the medication.

10. The information that the federal government requires to be dispensed with certain drugs is known as _____ .

11. The _____ route bypasses the first-pass effect and increases bioavailability.

12. The _____ route uses skin absorption as a mode of delivery for medication.

13. What are the advantages of electronic prescribing?

     _____

14. Why is it important to look at the original copy when entering a script into the computer system?

     _____

15. Having too many medications to take can cause a decrease in patient _____ .

16. Synthetic vaccines contain _____ that cause the body to form an immune response to a certain disease.

17. Histamine is produced in the _____ .

18. Nizatidine (Axid) is an example of an _____ blocker.

19. A histamine reaction causes _____ of blood vessels.

20. A(n) _____ label contains instructions for the patient, as well as the physician's name, the date the prescription was filled, and the drug's name.

Matching–Terms and Definitions

a. allergy

b. antigen

c. Beers list

d. buccal

e. compliance

f. e-prescribing

g. histamine

h. immunization

i. inhalation

j. inscription

k. instillation

l. intradermal

m. intramuscular

n. intrathecal

o. intravenous

p. medication reconciliation

q. morbidity

r. mortality

s. ophthalmic

t. oral

u. otic

v. polypharmacy

w. prescription

x. signa

y. subcutaneous

z. sublingual

aa. systemic

bb. topical

cc. three times daily

dd. twice a day

ee. vaccine

_____ 21. The providing of a complete and accurate drug profile to each health care provider who cares for a patient

_____ 22. A state of heightened sensitivity as a result of exposure to a particular substance

_____ 23. Administration of a medication through a vein, thereby avoiding the first-pass effect; abbreviated IV

_____ 24. A direction for medication to be dispensed to a patient, written by a physician or a qualified licensed prescriber and filled by a pharmacist; referred to as an order when the medication is requested in a hospital setting

_____ 25. Death rate from a particular disease

_____ 26. A list of drugs for which monitoring is especially important in elderly patients

_____ 27. To be placed between the cheek and the gums

_____ 28. A patient's adherence to the dose schedule and other particular requirements of the specified regimen

_____ 29. The process which allows a prescriber's computer system to talk to the pharmacy's computer system and the medication order/prescription is transmitted to the pharmacy

_____ 30. A chemical produced by the body that evokes the symptoms of an allergic reaction and is blocked by antihistamines

_____ 31. To be injected into the spinal column

_____ 32. To be injected into a muscle; abbreviated IM

_____ 33. To be injected into the skin

_____ 34. Administration of a medication drop by drop

_____ 35. Administration of a medication through the respiratory system

_____ 36. The process by which the immune system is stimulated to acquire protection against a specific disease; usually achieved by use of a vaccine

_____ 37. Applied to the surface of the skin or mucous membranes

_____ 38. A suspension of disease-causing organisms, or fragments of them, administered to induce active immunity to the disease

_____ 39. To be injected into the tissue just beneath the skin

_____ 40. To be placed under the tongue

_____ 41. To be administered through the eye

_____ 42. Administration of a medication by mouth in either solid form, as a tablet or capsule, or in liquid form, as a solution or syrup

_____ 43. The concurrent use of multiple medications

_____ 44. Administered in the ear

_____ 45. BID

_____ 46. Rate of occurrence of a diseased state or condition

_____ 47. TID

_____ 48. The molecule that an antibody recognizes

_____ 49. Part of a prescription that provides directions to be included on the label for the patient to follow in taking the medication

_____ 50. Part of a prescription that identifies the name of the drug, the dose, and the quantities of the ingredients

_____ 51. Pertaining to or affecting the body as a whole

Puzzling the Technician–Terms and Definitions

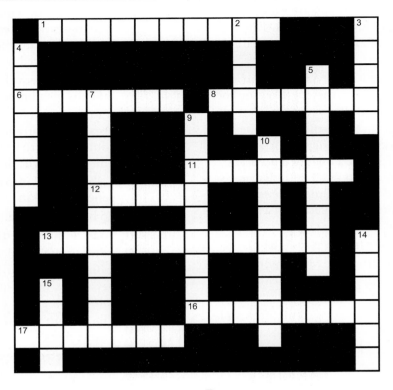

Across

1. intravenous, intracardiac, and intramuscular are examples of this route

6. a fragment of a protein molecule

8. portions of a disease-causing organism administered to produce immunity to that disease

11. administered by mouth

12. part of a prescription

13. physician's order to a pharmacist

16. affecting much of the entire body

17. container that assists patients with daily compliance

Down

2. route of drug administration through the ear

3. concentration of an antibody

4. what "cap" stands for

5. a natural biochemical that produces an allergic reaction

7. application of a drug to the skin

9. disease for which a vaccine is available for types A and B

10. rate of occurrence of a disease state

14. placing a drug between the cheek and gum

15. administered by ear

Unit

2

Major Classes of Pharmaceutical Products I

Antibiotics

4

Reading Drug Labels and Medication Orders

1. A patient brings in the prescription below. The drug label at the right shows the product available in the pharmacy.

> ℞ Amoxil 250 mg/5 mL suspension; take 1 tsp tid × 7 days

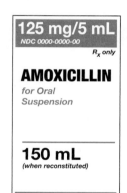

125 mg/5 mL
NDC 0000-0000-00
℞ only
AMOXICILLIN
for Oral
Suspension

150 mL
(when reconstituted)

a. The concentration requested in the prescription is unavailable. What would the dosing instructions be for the available product? Provide the answer in both teaspoonsfuls and milliliters. (*Note*: 1 tsp = 5 mL. Equivalencies are available in the Pharmacy Library section of the Internet Resource Center (IRC) for this textbook title at www.emcp.com.)

---

b. Using the drug shown in the label, how many milliliters would you dispense to meet the dosing requirements for the entire treatment period? (Do not assume any wasted medication.)

---

c. How many milligrams are prescribed for the patient to take in one day?

---

2. A prescription is written for Augmentin for strep throat. The insurance company refuses to pay for it. When you call the prescriber to change the drug, what do you recommend?

---

3. You receive the following prescription:

> ℞ Bactrim DS; 1 tab PO bid × 3d

Name _____ Date _____ **21**

a. What directions should be on the dispensed prescription label?

_____

b. How many tablets will be dispensed for the duration of therapy?

_____

4. You receive an order in your IV room for gentamicin 400 mg. How many milliliters of the following gentamicin would you use to make the dose?

_____

NDC 0000-0000-00

GENTAMICIN

Injection, USP equivalent to

40 mg/mL

20 mL multiple dose vial
For IM or IV use.   R_x only

5. You receive a script that is somewhat difficult to read. It is either ampicillin or amoxicillin. The drug is dosed three times a day. Which drug is it?

_____

6. Your hospital pharmacy makes a fortified tobramycin eyedrop that is 13.6% in a 10 mL bottle. How many milligrams of the drug are in the bottle of eyedrops?

_____

_____

7. You have an unusual order for intravitreal ceftazidime 2.25 mg/0.1 mL. Your pharmacy has ceftazidime already in solution at 100 mg/mL. Using 1 mL of that ceftazidime, how many milliliters of sodium chloride 0.9% would you have to add to prepare the proper concentration?

_____

_____

8. The following pediatric prescription is received by the pharmacy. The drug label at the right shows the drug to be dispensed.

_____

℞   clindamycin 285 mg PO q8 h

_____

100mL   NDC 0000-0000-00

CLINDAMYCIN

Oral Solution

75 mg/5 mL

R_x only

a. What are the correct dosing instructions, in milliliters, for the dispensed label?

_____

b. According to the label, how many doses are in the bottle?

_____

9. You receive an order for 1,200,000 units of penicillin G for a pediatric patient. The drug label shows the solution available in stock. How many milliliters will provide the dose required?

_____

_____

NDC 0000-0000-00

℞_x

PENICILLIN G POTASSIUM

FOR INJECTION USP

2,000,000 units

R_x only   50 mL vial

10. You receive the following prescription:

> ℞   Macrobid 100 mg PO bid × 14 days

    a. How should the dosing instructions on the dispensed label read?

    b. How many 100 mg capsules will be needed for a 14-day supply?

Understanding the Larger Medical Context

11. What is meant by the term *dose loading*?

12. Timmy Thompson is a 13-year-old boy who has severe acne. He is the star right fielder for his Little League team, and he intends to spend most of his summer outside playing baseball. The physician writes the following prescription for Timmy's acne:

> ℞   minocycline 100 mg PO daily

    a. What would you warn Timmy's parents about when they pick up the medication? Other than discontinuing the medication, how could this side effect be managed?

    b. How should Timmy change his diet while taking this medication?

13. Mr. Chin calls your pharmacy because he cannot read the instructions for his new Z-Pak prescription. He says, "I have six tablets. Should I take them all at once, or one a day? Should I take this drug on an empty stomach?" What are the instructions Mr. Chin needs to take his Z-Pak?

14. Make a list of the liquid antibiotics that must be stored in the refrigerator after reconstitution. (Keep a copy of this list in your pocket for quick reference during your rotations.)

15. Which antibiotic must be mixed in at least 250 mL of fluid and infused slowly to avoid red man's syndrome?

16. Which antibiotic is effective against fungi and protozoa as well as bacteria?

_____

17. Dr. Hoar is a pharmacist who likes to quiz pharmacy technicians about antibiotics. What do you answer when he asks you, "What is the only fourth-generation cephalosporin?"

_____

18. Why are cephalosporins the most widely used antibiotics?

_____

Dispensing and Storing Drugs

Where or how should the following medications be stored in the pharmacy?

19. Amoxil suspension before reconstitution

_____

20. amoxicillin-clavulanate suspension after reconstitution

_____

21. Bactrim suspension

_____

22. metronidazole tablets

_____

23. quinupristin-dalfopristin injection before reconstitution

_____

24. Synercid injection after reconstitution

_____

25. Reconstituted penicillin

_____

26. Tequin tablets

_____

27. reconstituted cefoxitin

_____

28. clindamycin oral solution

_____

Putting Safety First

Do the doses match the medications? If not, give a common dose.

29. amoxicillin 2 mg for prophylactic dose for dental procedures

   _____

30. Zithromax 1,000 mg prophylactic dose

   _____

31. amoxicillin qd

   _____

32. Fortaz mixed in NS only and placed in 50 mL bag administered over 30 minutes

   _____

33. Zithromax 1 gram for STD

   _____

Understanding Concepts

34. Which antibiotic is also effective against fungi? And, because of this, what infection is it often used to treat?

   _____

35. You get the following prescription for a 4-year-old patient:

   ℞ clindamycin 150 mg tid for 10 days

   Clindamycin comes in bottles of 100 mL at 75 mg/5 mL. (Remember, all reconstituted antibiotics must be shaken to get the proper dose, because they tend to settle.) What sig will you put on the bottle? How many bottles will you dispense? Where will you tell the parent to store it? What flavor is it?

   _____

36. The patient has the following prescription from the dentist:

   ℞ Penicillin 2 grams 30 minutes before procedure

   When you enter the prescription into the computer, it alerts you that the patient is allergic to penicillin. What do you do?

   _____

37. What medication options are available to a dentist who wishes to offer his or her patient a prophylaxis before a procedure?

   _____

38. List the antibiotics that must have a medication guide.

   _____

39. List the antibiotics that have a black box warning.

   _____

40. Which drug is only approved for C-Dif?

   _____

41. Ciprofloxacin comes both in otic and opthalmic forms. You receive a script that says:

   ℞   instill 4 gtt OA bid

   Which drug will you choose? What will be the sig on the bottle?

   _____

42. Your next script says:

   ℞   instill 1 gtt ou in the am and pm

   Which drug will you choose? How will the sig on the bottle read?

   _____

43. You then receive the following script for a 25-year-old patient:

   ℞   Bactrim DS BID × 10 days for UTI

   What generic drug will you dispense? What will the sig be? How many tablets will you dispense? What is UTI? After dispensing the medication, what will you do with the tray?

   _____

   _____

44. The patient, a 9 year old named LaTania, is prescribed Duricef. Her mother informs you that the child hates orange and will not take any drug that has an orange flavor. What do you do? (The answer involves some creative thinking not discussed in the chapter.)

   _____

   _____

Matching–Brand and Generic Drug Names

_____ 45. Adoxa

_____ 46. Amoxil

_____ 47. Augmentin

_____ 48. Bactrim DS

_____ 49. Cipro

_____ 50. Cleocin

_____ 51. Flagyl

_____ 52. Keflex

_____ 53. Omnicef

_____ 54. Z-Pak

a. amoxicillin

b. amoxicillin-clavulanate

c. azithromycin

d. cefdinir

e. cephalexin

f. doxycycline

g. ciprofloxacin

h. clindamycin

i. metronidazole

j. sulfamethoxazole-trimethoprim

Matching–Terms and Definitions

_____ 55. An antibiotic that is effective against multiple organisms

_____ 56. A drug that works by conversion of metabolic processes within the body

_____ 57. A condition in which bacteria grow in body tissues and cause tissue damage to the host either by their presence or by toxins they produce

_____ 58. A sometimes fatal form or erythema multiforme (an allergic reaction marked by red blotches on the skin)

_____ 59. Low blood pressure

_____ 60. A measurement of acidity or alkalinity

_____ 61. A new infection complicating the course of therapy of an existing infection

_____ 62. A systemic inflammatory response to infection resulting from blood-borne infections

_____ 63. Treatment begun before a definite diagnosis can be obtained

_____ 64. A chemical substance with the ability to kill or inhibit the growth of bacteria by interfering with bacteria life processes

a. antibiotic

b. broad-spectrum antibiotic

c. empirical treatment

d. hypotension

e. infection

f. pH

g. prodrug

h. sepsis

i. Stevens-Johnson syndrome

j. superinfection

Therapy for Fungal and Viral Infections

Reading Drug Labels and Medication Orders

1. You are presented with the following prescription, and the drug label shown is the product you pick up from the pharmacy shelf.

R℞ amphotericin B 60 mg IV in NS over 4 hours for 7 days

NDC 0000-0000-00

amphotericin B
for injection, USP

50 mg
Sterile
FOR INTRAVENOUS INFUSION ONLY
STOP: Verify the product name and dosage if dose exceeds 1.5 mg/kg.

℞ only
See insert for reconstitution and dosage information.
Store under refrigeration 2° to 8°C (36° to 46°F).
For intravenous infusion only. Protect from light during administration. Each vial contains 50 mg amphotericin B and 41 mg sodium desoxycholate buffered with 20.2 mg sodium phosphates (consisting of mono and dibasic sodium phosphate, phosphoric acid and sodium hydroxide).

LOT **S**
EXP **L**

a. Is normal saline an appropriate diluent for amphotericin? If yes, explain why. If no, explain why not and provide an appropriate diluent.

_____

_____

b. Assuming the patient receives the full seven days of therapy, how many total grams will be administered? Show your calculation.

_____

c. How many vials should you have on hand to last the seven days? Explain.

_____

_____

2. You are presented with the following prescription, and the drug label shows that the product is available in the pharmacy in 500 mg caplets.

> ℞   Valtrex (valacyclovir) 1 g PO bid × 10 days

   a. How many caplets will you dispense? Explain your answer.

         _____

         _____

         _____

   b. How will the instructions read on the label?

         _____

3. Ms. Roselli brings in the following prescription for her son Joey. Because Joey cannot swallow tablets, she asks you to fill the prescription with a liquid form. You have amantadine syrup 50 mg/5 mL in stock. (*Note*: 1 tsp = 5 mL. Equivalencies are available in the Pharmacy Library section of the Internet Resource Center (IRC) for this textbook title at www.emcp.com.)

> ℞   amantadine 100 mg PO bid × 3 days

   a. How many milliliters are in one dose?

         _____

   b. How many teaspoonsful are in one dose?

         _____

   c. How will the instructions read on the prescription label?

         _____

   d. How many milliliters will you dispense?

         _____

4. The following order is received by the hospital pharmacy for a patient who weighs 84 lb. (*Note*: 1 kg = 2.2 lb. Equivalencies are available in the Pharmacy Library section of the Internet Resource Center (IRC) for this textbook title at www.paradigmcollege.net/pharmacology5e.)

R̲x̲   acyclovir 10 mg/kg IV q8 h

a. What is the total amount of acyclovir per dose?

b. Using a 50 mg/mL vial, how many milliliters would you use per day?

c. The maximum concentration for acyclovir to be infused is 7 mg/mL. What is the minimum volume to administer this dose? Use the intravenous solutions available commercially (50 mL, 100 mL, 150 mL, 250 mL, 500 mL, and 1000 mL).

5. Chapter 3 contains a list of drugs that must be dispensed in the original containers. Which drugs found in this chapter are on that list?

6. You receive the following prescription, and the drug label shows that the product is available:

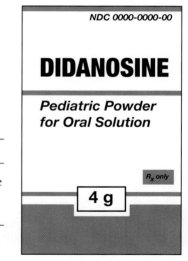

R̲x̲   Videx (didanosine) suspension 100 mg PO bid

NDC 0000-0000-00

DIDANOSINE

Pediatric Powder for Oral Solution

R̲x̲ only

4 g

a. How would you reconstitute the powder in the bottle?

b. What volume of didanosine liquid would the patient take per day?

c. Assuming that the dose does not change, how many days will a 200 mL bottle last?

7. What are the advantages of pulse dosing?

8. You receive the following prescription, and the drug label indicates that the drug is available as 250 mg capsules:

> $\text{R}\!\!\!/$ ganciclovir 500 mg PO bid

a. How many capsules will be required for a one-month supply? Show your calculations.

_____

_____

b. What are other dosage forms for ganciclovir?

_____

9. You receive the following prescription:

> $\text{R}\!\!\!/$ saquinavir 600 mg PO tid on an empty stomach

a. Which brand name is the patient most likely taking? Explain your answer.

_____

b. What auxiliary labels would you affix to the prescription vial?

_____

10. You receive the following prescription. The drug label shown at right is the medication available in the pharmacy:

> $\text{R}\!\!\!/$ nystatin 1 tsp swish and swallow 4 times daily

a. How long will the bottle last if no doses are missed? Show your calculations.

_____

_____

b. If the patient is to receive therapy for one week, how many bottles would you dispense? Show your calculations.

_____

_____

60mL   NDC 0000-0000-00

100,000 units per mL

NYSTATIN

ORAL
SUSPENSION USP

**Shake well
before using**

Caution: Federal law prohibits
dispensing without prescription

Understanding the Larger Medical Context

11. You receive a prescription for VFend with instructions to mix it ASAP. Two hours later, the order is cancelled. What do you do with the mixed drug?

    _____

    _____

12. Which medications are prescribed to patients who have or have been exposed to influenza?

    _____

13. Which NNRTI can cause a patient to test positive when taking a cannabinoid (marijuana) test?

    _____

14. Which protease inhibitor will cause the patient to turn yellow if the drug is administered correctly?

    _____

15. Atripla is a combination of which three drugs?

    _____

Dispensing and Storing Drugs

16. Which HIV drug must be dispensed with a card for the patient to carry at all times?

    _____

17. With which antiviral should you use chemotherapeutic precautions?

    _____

18. Which antivirals are available in both intravenous and by-mouth dosage forms?

    _____

19. Which antiviral is an ocular agent?

    _____

20. Which antiviral comes as either a capsule or a syrup but is not approved to be used in children?

    _____

21. Which HIV medication should be dispensed with alcohol pads to clean the injection site before administration?

    _____

22. Which liquid antiviral contains alcohol but is approved to be used in children?

    _____

23. A dose of intravenous acyclovir has already been made. Would you store it in the refrigerator or at room temperature?

_____

24. Which antiviral might a pharmacy stock but never dispense directly to a patient?

_____

25. Which four drug classes constitute HAART?

_____

26. Which antifungal is normally dispensed in liquid form, often with a sig that reads "swish and swallow"?

_____

27. Which antiviral is an ocular agent?

_____

28. Which protease inhibitor must be dispensed in the original container?

_____

29. Why have manufacturers of HIV drugs moved to drug combinations?

_____

30. Which three drugs should not be given with stavudine?

_____

Putting Safety First

Does the requested dose match the typical medication dose in the following orders? If not, provide the typical dosage for each medication.

31. Lamisil 250 mg PO bid

_____

32. Anidulafungin has a loading dose of 400 mg.

_____

33. Amantadine is packaged in 500 mg doses.

_____

34. Cytovene is dosed at 250 mg and 500 mg.

_____

35. Relenza 2 inhalations bid q12 h for 10 days

_____

Understanding Concepts

36. Three drugs out of which four classes constitute HAART?

_____

37. What orders should accompany amphotericin B in order to avoid side effects?

_____

38. Which antifungal agent kills the fungus and persists longer in the nail than other anti-fungal drugs?

_____

39. Which drug is a combination of lopinavir and ritonavir?

_____

40. Why would a female need to take an antifungal with an antibiotic?

_____

41. What is a troche, and which antifungal comes as a troche?

_____

42. To which drug class do abacavair and lamivudine belong?

_____

43. What does PEP stand for?

_____

44. List three steps to avoid HIV.

_____

_____

_____

45. Which NNRTI decreases the effectiveness of birth control pills?

_____

46. Atripla is a combination of which three drug classes? Why does it have a Black Box warning?

_____

_____

47. Which other drugs in this chapter have a Black Box warning?

_____

48. Which drugs must be dispensed with a medication guide?

_____

Matching–Terms and Definitions

_____ 49. One drug given to increase the serum concentration of another drug

_____ 50. An eukaroyotic sterol that in higher animals is the precursor of bile acids and steroid hormones and is a key constituent of cell membranes

_____ 51. Tamiflu

_____ 52. A regimen of dosing one week per month; commonly used for treating fungal nail infections

_____ 53. Norvir

_____ 54. Viral inflammation of the liver

_____ 55. A substance that exerts virus-nonspecific but host-specific antiviral activity by inducing genes coding for antiviral proteins that inhibit the synthesis of viral RNA

_____ 56. The ability of a virus to lie dormant and then, under certain conditions reproduce and again behave like an infective agent, causing cell damage

_____ 57. A retrovirus transmitted in body fluids that causes acquired immune deficiency syndrome (AIDS) by attacking T lymphocytes

_____ 58. Having a deficiency in the immune response system

a. boost

b. cholesterol

c. hepatitis

d. human immunodeficiency virus (HIV)

e. immunocompromised

f. interferon

g. latency

h. Oseltamivir

i. Pulse dosing

j. Ritonivir

Matching–Antiviral and Antifungal Drugs

Identify whether the drug is an antiviral (V) or an antifungal (F).

_____ 59. Mycostatin

_____ 60. terazole

_____ 61. Zovirax

_____ 62. cidofovir

_____ 63. Valtrex

_____ 64. abacavir

_____ 65. Viread

_____ 66. andalafungin

_____ 67. Lamisil

_____ 68. voriconazole

_____ 69. Sporanox

_____ 70. If a drug ends in -_vir_, it is most likely from which class of drugs?

_____ 71. If a drug ends in -_zole_, it is most likely from which class of drugs?

Anesthetics and Narcotics

6

Reading Drug Labels and Medication Orders

1. In the outpatient pharmacy, you receive the following prescription:

   ℞   Vicodin 5/500 2 tab q4 h prn pain #150

   a. Is this prescription okay to dispense? Explain your answer.

   _____

   b. If the patient takes the prescription as written, what would be the total daily dose of acetaminophen?

   _____

2. What is the fifth vital sign?

   _____

3. What is a PCA? Explain the concept.

   _____

   _____

   _____

4. What drug is used as the standard against which all other narcotic analgesics are measured?

   _____

5. What is the chemotrigger zone?

   _____

   _____

6. What are the two categories of treatment for migraine headaches?

   _____

7. How should persistent pain be treated? (Hint: analgesic ladder)

_____

8. Why are the acetaminophen and aspirin components of combination narcotic-analgesic drugs important?

_____

_____

9. Why are neuromuscular blocking agents important?

_____

10. When is prophylactic treatment indicated for migraines?

_____

11. Which drug is approved for the treatment of hiccups?

_____

Understanding the Larger Medical Context

12. The most common neurotransmitter in the brain is _____, and it is always excitatory.

13. You work in a children's hospital. Many inhaled anesthetics are kept in stock, but desflurane is not. Why is desflurane unavailable?

_____

_____

14. What is the dose equivalent of Percocet to 10 mg IM morphine?

_____

15. Which class of local anesthetic should be avoided in patients with liver insufficiency?

_____

16. Is ketamine (Ketalar) an appropriate anesthetic for a patient with uncontrolled hypertension? Why or why not?

_____

_____

17. Does the autonomic nervous system regulate body systems under voluntary or involuntary control?

_____

18. What are the five components of a classic migraine headache?

_____

_____

19. What is the class of drug for eletriptan (Relpax)?

20. What dosage forms are commercially available for metoclopramide (Reglan)?

21. Why would you find flumazenil (Romazicon) in an emergency room kit? What are possible side effects of flumazenil?

Dispensing and Storing Drugs

22. Which group of pharmacy personnel usually checks in CII drugs?

23. Which class of drugs must have the original prescription in the pharmacy?

24. Can C-IIs be e-scribed?

25. What form is used when ordering C-IIs?

26. Some pharmacies require a count back on some controlled substances. Explain why this is done and what it involves.

Putting Safety First

27. Lidocaine and Duragesic both come as patches to control pain. Which one may be cut?

28. For how long are C-IIIs and C-IVs good?

29. How many refills are allowed on C-IIIs and C-IVs?

30. How many refills are allowed on C-IIs?

31. Why are the above classes of drugs limited as to dates and refills?

Understanding Concepts

32. The only neurotransmitter of the parasympathetic nervous system is _____.

33. The only neurotransmitter of the somatic nervous system is _____.

34. The drug derived from fungi and used for migraine treatment is _____.

35. _____ anesthesia: characterized by reversible unconsciousness.

36. The abbreviation for the part of a hospital that provides intensive care is _____.

37. A compulsive disorder that leads to continued use of a drug is _____.

38. CTZ stands for _____.

39. An _____ aura is a sensation that precedes the onset of a migraine headache.

40. A severe headache may be a _____.

41. _____ is the abbreviation of the body system that involves transmittance of electrical signals.

42. Indicate the drug class for each of the following drugs:

    a. hydromorphone _____

    b. hydrocodone _____

    c. oxycodone _____

    d. morphine _____

    e. diazepam _____

Matching–Brand and Generic Drug Names

_____ 43. acetaminophen-codeine

_____ 44. diazepam

_____ 45. hydrocodone-acetaminophen

_____ 46. lorazepam

_____ 47. metoclopramide

_____ 48. oxycodone-acetaminophen

_____ 49. hydromorphone

_____ 50. sumatriptan

a. Ativan

b. Dilaudid

c. Imitrex

d. Percocet

e. Lortab

f. Reglan

g. Tylenol with codeine

h. Valium

Matching–Terms and Definitions

_____ 51. addiction

_____ 52. analgesic

_____ 53. analgesic ladder

_____ 54. antagonists

_____ 55. aura

_____ 56. autonomic nervous system

_____ 57. beta-1 receptors

_____ 58. beta-2 receptors

_____ 59. central nervous system

_____ 60. dependence

_____ 61. general anesthesia

_____ 62. local anesthesia

_____ 63. malignant hyperthermia

_____ 64. migraine headache

_____ 65. narcotic analgesic

_____ 66. neurotransmitter

_____ 67. nonsteroidal
       anti-inflammatory drug

a. A chemical substance that is selectively released from a neuron and stimulates or inhibits activity in the neuron's target cell

b. A compulsive disorder that leads to continued use of a drug despite harm to the user

c. A condition characterized by reversible unconsciousness, analgesia, skeletal muscle relaxation, and amnesia on recovery

d. A drug such as aspirin or ibuprofen that reduces pain and inflammation

e. A drug that alleviates pain

f. A guideline for selecting pain-relieving medications according to the severity of the pain and whether agents lower on the ladder have been able to control the pain

g. A physical and emotional reliance on a drug

h. A rare, but serious, side effect of anesthesia associated with an increase in intracellular calcium and a rapid rise in body temperature

i. A severe throbbing unilateral headache, usually accompanied by nausea, photophobia, phonophobia, and hyperesthesia

j. A subjective sensation or motor phenomenon that precedes and marks the onset of a migraine headache

k. Drugs used to reverse the effects of other drugs, such as in treatment of benzodiazepine or narcotic overdoses

l. Nerve receptors on the heart that control the rate and strength of the heartbeat in response to epinephrine

m. Nerve receptors that control vasodilation and relaxation of the smooth muscle of the airways in response to epinephrine

n. Pain medication containing an opioid

o. The brain and spinal cord

p. The part of the efferent system of the PNS that regulates activities of body structures not under voluntary control

q. The production of transient and reversible loss of sensation in a defined area of the body

Psychiatric and Related Drugs

7

Reading Drug Labels and Medication Orders

1. You receive a prescription that indicates the patient is to take "500 mg qam for 10 days." The medication is available in 250 mg tablets.

   a. How many tablets will the patient take in a day?

   _____

   b. How many tablets will be dispensed?

   _____

2. You receive the following prescription. Celexa comes in 240 mL bottles, in an oral solution of 10 mg/5 mL.

   ℞   Celexa Liq 30 mg every day

   a. How much liquid will be in each dose?

   _____

   b. How long will the bottle last the patient?

   _____

Understanding the Larger Medical Context

3. What is the most common side effect of tricyclic antidepressants?

   _____

4. What side effect of some antipsychotic medications causes involuntary movements and may be irreversible?

   _____

5. Why is clozapine not more commonly used?

   _____

   _____

   _____

6. List the three criteria for choosing anti-psychotic drugs.

   _____

   _____

   _____

7. Which antidepressant works only on dopamine receptors?

   _____

8. What are the major effects of long-term alcoholism on the body?

   _____

   _____

9. MAOIs have many side effects and are not much used in psychotic disorders. What other use do these drugs have?

   _____

10. Which drugs discussed in this chapter are Schedule II controlled substances?

   _____

Dispensing and Storing Drugs

11. Which class of medications is used only for insomnia?

    _____

12. With which drug will patients commonly self-medicate their anxiety or insomnia?

    _____

13. What are the effects of tardive dyskinesia?

    _____

14. Which drug is stored near and could easily be confused with Celebrex?

    _____

15. Which drug is stored near and often confused with Pepcid because the strengths are the same?

    _____

16. Which antianxiety agent might be confused with Zantac, if ordered verbally?

    _____

17. Which drugs in this chapter, as a class, must have a medication guide?

    _____

18. Which tricyclic antidepressant is used in the liquid form by dentists to treat "burning mouth" syndrome?

    _____

    _____

Fill in the blanks with the control schedule for each of the following drugs.

_____ 19. aripiprazole (Abilify)

_____ 20. secobarbital (Seconal)

_____ 21. zolpidem (Ambien)

_____ 22. fluoxetine (Prozac)

_____ 23. benzodiazepines

_____ 24. modafinil (Provigil)

_____ 25. eszopiclone (Lunesta)

_____ 26. ramelton (Rozerem)

_____ 27. paroxetine (Paxil)

_____ 28. risperdone (Risperdal)

Putting Safety First

29. Why should trazedone be avoided in young males?

_____

30. You receive the following prescription:

_____

R℞   Xanax 1 mg tid #90 refills 11

_____

Can you fill the prescription as written? Why or why not?

_____

31. A prescription for a C-II is presented to you. It has two refills on it and no DEA. Can this prescription be filled? Why?

_____

32. You receive the following script:

_____

R℞   Keflex 200 mg qid #20. 0 refills

      Lortab 5 qid prn pain #60 2 refills

_____

The Lortab order is in different handwriting, and there is no DEA. Can this prescription be filled? What do you think is going on here?

_____

Understanding Concepts

33. Which drug can be used both for schizophrenia and bipolar disorder?

_____

34. Which drug has consistently been shown to decrease the risk of suicide for bipolar patients?

_____

35. Which drug was the first approved to treat autism?

_____

36. Which drug is used to control episodes of laughing and crying?

_____

37. List the four steps toward recovery for alcoholics.

_____

_____

_____

_____

38. Which tricyclic antidepressant is used for bed wetting in children?

_____

39. Which drug is approved as an aid to smoking sensation?

_____

40. Which hypnotic is not a controlled substance?

_____

41. What is the brand name of haloperidol?

_____

42. Which Z hypnotic drug is approved for sleep onset insomnia?

_____

43. Which drug is prescribed for bipolar disorder and is also the name of a metal?

_____

44. What is the generic name for Seroquel?

_____

45. What is the brand name for temazepam?

_____

46. Which drug is referred to as Prozac with a punch?

_____

47. Which chronic psychotic disorder is marked by delusions, bizarre behavior, withdrawal, and abnormalities in perception and content of thought?

_____

48. What is the advantage of prescribing bupropion over other antidepressants for elderly males?

_____

49. _____ is an intense, overwhelming, and uncontrollable anxiety.

50. _____ dyskinesia is characterized by involuntary movements of the mouth, lips, and tongue.

51. _____ is a state of uneasiness and apprehension.

52. _____ is an osmotic-controlled release oral delivery system.

53. _____ is a condition characterized by a disinterest in eating.

54. _____ disorder is a condition in which patients swing between major depression and agitation.

55. Difficulty falling and/or staying asleep is referred to as _____.

56. _____ was originally referred to as shell shock.

57. _____ is a form of depression that occurs in fall and winter.

Matching–Brand and Generic Drug Names

_____ 58. alprazolam

_____ 59. bupropion

_____ 60. buspirone

_____ 61. citalopram

_____ 62. diazepam

_____ 63. escitalopram

_____ 64. eszopiclone

_____ 65. fluoxetine

_____ 66. lorazepam

_____ 67. olanzaprine

_____ 68. quetiapine

_____ 69. risperdone

_____ 70. temazepam

_____ 71. topiramate

_____ 72. trazedone

_____ 73. venlafaxine

_____ 74. zolpidem

a. Ambien

b. Ativan

c. BuSpar

d. Celexa

e. Desyrel

f. Effexor

g. Lexapro

h. Lunesta

i. Prozac

j. Restoril

k. Risperdal

l. Seroquel

m. Topamax

n. Valium

o. Wellbutrin

p. Xanax

q. Zyprexa

Matching–Terms and Definitions

_____ 75. A condition in which a patient presents with mood swings that alternate between periods of major depression and periods of mild to severe chronic agitation

_____ 76. A state of uneasiness characterized by apprehension and worry about possible events

_____ 77. A possibly fatal condition caused by combining antidepressants that increase serotonin levels with other medications that also stimulate serotonin receptors

_____ 78. A class of antidepressant drugs, developed earlier than the SSRIs and SNRIs, that also prevent neuron reuptake of norepinephrine and/or serotonin

_____ 79. An antidepressant drug that inhibits the activity of the enzymes that break down catecholamines (such as norepinephrine) and serotonin

_____ 80. Empty shell of an OROS tablet, excreted in the stool after the drug has dissolved

_____ 81. A drug that induces sleep

_____ 82. An antidepressant drug that blocks the reuptake of serotonin with little effect on norepinephrine and fewer side effects than other antidepressant drugs

_____ 83. A drug delivery system that allows the drug to dissolve through pores in the tablet shell; the empty shell, called a ghost, tablet is passed in the stool

a. anxiety

b. bipolar disorder

c. ghost

d. hypnotic

e. monoamine oxidase inhibitor (MAOIs)

f. osmotic-controlled release oral delivery system (OROS)

g. selective serotonin reuptake inhibitor (SSRI)

h. serotonin syndrome

i. tricyclic antidepressant (TCA)

Drugs for Central Nervous System Disorders

8

Reading Drug Labels and Medication Orders

1. You receive the following prescription. What is the problem with the prescription as written?

   R_x Clonazepam 0.5 mg 1 tid #90 refill × 11

2. You receive the following prescription, and the drug label shown is the product available in the pharmacy. How many tablets will you dispense? Show your calculations.

   R_x Dilantin 50 mg bid × 2 days, then 50 mg qid × 8 days

NDC 0000-0000-00

Phenytoin

50 mg

*Caution: Federal law prohibits
dispensing without prescription*

100 tablets

---

3. You receive the following order for a patient who weighs 88 kg. The pharmacy has azathioprine in 100 mg vials.

℞   Imuran IV 1.75 mg/kg/day

   a. What is the daily dose? Show your calculations.

   _____

   b. Is this the correct product?

   _____

   c. How much product would be used in a six-day supply? Show your calculations.

   _____

Understanding the Larger Medical Context

4. What are the different types of generalized seizures?

   _____

   _____

5. Loss of dopaminergic neurons from which region of the brain leads to Parkinson's disease?

   _____

6. What is the benefit of levodopa-carbidopa compared to levodopa alone?

   _____

   _____

   _____

   _____

7. What is the most common reason for drug therapy failure in epilepsy?

   _____

   _____

8. What are the first-line treatments and route of administration for status epilepticus?

   _____

   _____

   _____

9. What are signs and symptoms of myasthenia gravis?

_____

_____

_____

_____

10. Which three drugs are approved to treat fibromyalgia?

_____

Dispensing and Storing Drugs

Where or how should the following medications be stored in the pharmacy?

11. glatiramer acetate (Copaxone)

_____

12. phenytoin suspension

_____

13. methylphenidate

_____

14. interferon beta-1a (Avonex)

_____

15. donepezil (Aricept)

_____

What auxiliary labels would you put on the following medications?

16. tacrine (Cognex)

_____

17. interferon beta-1a (Avonex)

_____

18. Which drug class in this chapter requires a medication guide?

_____

19. Intuniv is the ER form of which drug?

_____

20. List the drugs in this chapter that require a medication guide. Remember to list them individually, not as a class.

_____

Name the control schedule for each of the following drugs.

_____ 21. clonazepam (Klonopin)

_____ 22. dexmethylphenidate (Focalin)

_____ 23. dextroamphetamine-amphetamine (Adderall)

_____ 24. diazepam (Valium)

_____ 25. lisdexamphetamine (Vyvanse)

_____ 26. lorazepam (Ativan)

_____ 27. methylphenidate (Concerta)

_____ 28. phenobarbital (Luminal Sodium)

_____ 29. pregabalin (Lyrica)

Putting Safety First

Does the requested dose match the typical medication dose in the following orders? If not, provide the typical dosage for each medication.

30. Zarontin bid to achieve therapeutic plasma concentrations

_____

31. Keppra should be given in doses greater than 300 mg to be effective.

_____

_____

32. Zelapar daily dose should not exceed 10 mg.

_____

33. Concerta bid

_____

34. Interferon beta-1a administered every other day

_____

Understanding Concepts

35. You receive the following prescription:

> ℞ Banzel 400 mg bid dispense one month's supply 5 refills

Banzel comes in tablets, so how will this be mixed? What will be the sig on the script?

_____

36. Which drug can be used to diagnose myasthenia gravis? _____

37. _____ acid is an anticonvulsant.

38. _____ is a combination of levodopa, carbidopa, and entacapone?

39. _____ is the generic for Klonopin.

40. A _____ mal seizure is the most serious form of seizure.

41. _____ gravis is a disorder of the interface between nerves and muscles resulting in the muscles being unresponsive to nerve signals to move them.

42. _____ is an autoimmune disease that affects the myelin sheath.

43. _____ is a paralytic drooping of the upper eyelids.

44. The _____ oblongata is a part of the brain.

45. _____ leg syndrome is a twitching, uneasiness, aching, or burning in the legs that occurs primarily after retiring to bed.

46. _____ is a chronic aching and stiffness with a lack of stamina.

47. _____ epilepticus is a serious disorder involving continuous tonic-clonic convulsions.

48. A _____ seizure is localized in a specific area of the brain and almost always results from injury to the cerebral cortex.

49. _____ is a neurological disorder that involves sudden and recurring seizures.

50. Which hypertension drug is used to treat ADHD? _____

51. Which drug used to treat Parkinson's is an MAOI? _____

52. Which three attention deficit drugs are not C-IIs?

_____

53. _____ is the most commonly used drug in Parkinson's disease.

54. _____ is referred to as the son of gabapentin.

Matching–Brand and Generic Drug Names

_____ 55. atomoxetine

_____ 56. clonazepam

_____ 57. dextroamphetamine-amphetamine

_____ 58. divalproex

_____ 59. gabapentin

_____ 60. lamotrigine

_____ 61. valproic acid

a. Adderall

b. Depakene

c. Depakote

d. Klonpin

e. Lamictal

f. Neurontin

g. Strattera

Matching–Terms and Definitions

_____ 62. adjunct

_____ 63. Alzheimer disease

_____ 64. amyotrophic lateral sclerosis

_____ 65. anticonvulsant

_____ 66. attention-deficit hyperactivity disorder (ADHD)

_____ 67. area under the curve

_____ 68. dysphagia

_____ 69. isomer

_____ 70. on-off phenomenon

_____ 71. Parkinson disease

_____ 72. restless leg syndrome

_____ 73. seizure

_____ 74. status epilepticus

_____ 75. substance P

a. A degenerative disorder of the brain that leads to progressive dementia and changes in personality and behavior

b. A degenerative disease of the motor nerves; also called Lou Gehrig's disease

c. A drug to control seizures

d. A drug used with another drug

e. A measure of drug concentration in the blood

f. A neurological disorder characterized by akinesia, resting tremor, and muscle rigidity

g. A neurological disorder characterized by hyperactivity, impulsivity, and distractibility

h. A potent neurotransmitter mediating sensations of pain, touch, and temperature

i. Difficulty swallowing

j. An overpowering urge to move the legs, especially at rest

k. A serious disorder involving tonic-clonic convulsions that last at least 30 minutes

l. Involuntary contraction or series of contractions of the voluntary muscles

m. One of two or more compounds that contain the same number and type of atoms but have different molecular structures

n. A wide fluctuation between abnormally increased and abnormally diminished motor function, present in many Parkinson's patients after about five years of levodopa therapy

Respiratory Drugs

9

Reading Drug Labels and Medication Orders

1. Mr. Gaines brings in a prescription for the following cough syrup:

   ℞ Robitussin A-C 1 tsp PO q4-q6 h prn persistent cough

   a. How would you express the directions on the label?

   _____

   _____

   Guaifenesin Syrup and Dextrometh
   100 mg/10 mg per 5 mL

   120 mL

   b. What auxiliary labels would you add to this prescription bottle? Explain.

   _____

   _____

2. Ms. Marcos presents the following prescription to the pharmacy:

   ℞ Nicotine lozenge PO q4 h prn cravings

   If Ms. Marcos uses the maximum number of lozenges every day, how many would she need for a month? Show your calculations.

   _____

   _____

Name _____ Date _____

3. You receive the following order in the pharmacy:

> ℞   Singulair 10 mg chew one tab PO daily

   a. Which dosage forms for Singulair are available for this order?

   b. How many tablets would you supply for one month? Show your calculations.

4. Orapred comes in two strengths, 15 mg/5 mL and 5 mg/5 mL. You receive the following prescription in the pharmacy:

> ℞   Orapred 9 mg PO every day for 10 days

   a. If you dispense from the 15 mg/mL bottle, how much would you dispense and what would be the dose? Show your calculations.

   b. If you dispense from the 5 mg/mL bottle, how much would you dispense and what would be the dose? Show your calculations.

5. You receive the following prescription:

> ℞   rifampin 300 mg PO daily

How many 150 mg capsules would the patient require for a three-month supply? Show your calculations.

6. You receive the following order:

> ℞   Vistaril 50 mg PO qhs

   a. Based on the prescription, which generic product would you dispense?

   b. What are all the dosage forms available for Vistaril?

7. You receive the following prescription:

Rx   Claritin 10 mg daily

What dosage form would be appropriate for the nasogastric route? For the nasogastric route, a plastic tube is inserted through the nose, down the back of the throat, through the esophagus, and into the stomach.

Understanding the Larger Medical Context

8. You receive the following prescription. Which brand name product would you expect to dispense? Explain your answer.

Rx   fluticasone 50 mcg, 1 spray daily in each nostril

9. Mr. Usher takes the following regimen for his asthma:

Rx   Advair 250/50 1 puff bid

What should Mr. Usher do after taking his dose of Advair?

10. When using inhalers, what is the main difference between the HFA MDI inhaler compared to the dry-powder MDI inhaler?

11. List the benefits of not smoking.

Dispensing and Storing Drugs

12. Where should Spiriva capsules be kept?

    _____

13. Who puts the beyond use date on the Spiriva box?

    _____

14. You receive the following prescription:

    > ℞   Duoneb 0.5mg/2.5mg per nebulizer every 4 hours dispense 1 month's supply

    How many mLs will be charged to the insurance company? _____
    (Duoneb comes 0.5mg/2.5mg/3 mL.)

15. Mr. Mkembe brings you this prescription:

    > ℞   Ipatropium 0.02% (500 us/2.5) use 500 ug in nebulizer qid.
    >   Dispense one month's supply.

    How many mLs will be billed to the insurance company? _____

16. Which device is dispensed with a metered dose inhaler to help get the drug into the lungs?

    _____

17. Which medication should receive an auxiliary label that reads, "Do not use for more than three consecutive days"?

    _____

Putting Safety First

18. Little Johnnie Sparza is using his nebulizer correctly, but he constantly gets bronchial infections. Casually, you ask his mother how often she cleans the nebulizer. She replies "Oh, every now and then."

    a. What might be the source of Johnnie's infections?

       _____

    b. Explain to Johnny's mother how often she should clean the nebulizer.

       _____

19. Which drug is made from human plasma and therefore carries the risk of transmitting infections?

    _____

Understanding Concepts

20. _____ is a reversible lung disease.

21. _____ is the addictive component of tobacco.

22. _____ is an agent that destroys mucus.

23. _____ is the measurement used to assess the severity of asthma.

24. _____ is a device used with inhaled medicines.

25. MDI stands for _____.

26. _____ is the drug used in most rescue inhalers.

27. Dulera contains which two drugs? _____

28. What is an isomer?

_____

29. Which antihistamine rescue inhaler supposedly does not leave a bad taste in the mouth?

_____

Matching–Brand and Generic Drug Names

_____ 30. Advair Diskus

_____ 31. Allegra

_____ 32. Clarinex

_____ 33. Mucinex

_____ 34. Mucinex D

_____ 35. Nasonex

_____ 36. Robitussin A-C

_____ 37. Singulair

_____ 38. Tussionex

_____ 39. Zyrtec

a. cetirizine

b. desloratadine

c. guaifenesin-codeine

d. guaifenesin-pseudoephedrine

e. fluticasone-salmeterol

f. fexofenadine

g. guaifenesin

h. mometasone

i. montelukast

j. hydrocodone-chlorpheniramine

Matching–Terms and Definitions

_____ 40. antihistamines

_____ 41. asthma

_____ 42. antitussives

_____ 43. beyond use date

_____ 44. bronchitis

_____ 45. corticosteroid

_____ 46. cough suppressant

_____ 47. cystic fibrosis

_____ 48. decongestant

_____ 49. expectorant

_____ 50. guaifenesin

_____ 51. metered dose inhaler (MDI)

_____ 52. mucolytic

_____ 53. nebulizer

_____ 54. pseudoephedrine

_____ 55. RDS

_____ 56. rhinitis medicamentosa

_____ 57. spacer

_____ 58. varenicline

_____ 59. xanthine derivative

a. A condition of decreased response that results when nasal decongestants are used over prolonged periods

b. A condition in which the inner lining of the bronchial airways becomes inflamed, causing the expiration of air from the lungs to be obstructed

c. A device that delivers a specific amount of medication (as for asthma) in a fine enough spray to reach the innermost parts of the lungs using a puff of compressed gas

d. A device used in the administration of inhaled medications, using air flowing past a liquid to create a mist

e. A device used with a metered dose inhaler (MDI) to decrease the amount of spray deposited on the back of the throat and swallowed

f. A drug that causes relaxation of the airway smooth muscle, thus causing airway dilation and better air movement

g. A drug that chemically resembles substances produced by the adrenal gland and acts as an anti-inflammatory agent to suppress the immune response by stimulating adenylate cyclase

h. A reversible lung disease with intermittent attacks in which inspiration is obstructed; provoked by airborne allergens

i. An agent that causes the mucous membranes to shrink, thereby allowing the sinus cavities to drain

j. An agent that decreases the thickness and stickiness of mucus, enabling the patient to rid the lungs and airway of mucus when coughing

k. An agent that destroys or dissolves mucus

l. Common term for drugs that block the H_1 receptors

m. Drugs that block or suppress the act of coughing

n. CF

o. date after which drug should no longer be used

p. dextromethorphan

q. Mucinex

r. stop smoking drug that causes strange dreams

s. Sudafed

t. Respiratory Distress Syndrome

Major Classes of Pharmaceutical Products II

Drugs for Gastrointestinal and Related Diseases

10

Reading Drug Labels and Medication Orders

1. A patient comes into your pharmacy with the following prescription. If the patient took this medication as frequently as the prescription allows, how long would it take for a pint-sized bottle to run out? Show your calculations.

> ℞ Maalox 1 tbsp PO tid prn heartburn

_____

_____

2. Mr. Griffiths has been diagnosed with recurrent gallstones. He is currently using Actigall at prophylaxis doses. The physician has written the following prescription. Based on the smallest available capsule size for this medication, how many capsules will Mr. Griffiths receive in a month?

> ℞ Actigall 300 mg PO bid

_____

3. Mrs. Sim has been given a prescription for Enulose, and the following drug label shows the product available in the pharmacy.

> ℞ lactulose 2 tbsp PO q6 h prn constipation

a. How many grams of lactulose will Mrs. Sim get in a dose? Explain.

_____

_____

b. How many doses can Mrs. Sim get from a bottle of lactulose, assuming no waste? Show your calculations.

_____

c. How many days of treatment will a bottle last if Mrs. Sim takes the maximum dosage per day? Show your calculations.

_____

_____

4. Mr. Nasser is on mesalamine 800 mg PO tid.

a. Which brand name product should Mr. Nasser receive?

_____

b. What will be the directions on the medication label?

_____

16 Fl Oz (473 mL)

NDC 0000-0000-00

Lactulose Syrup USP

10 g/15 mL

FOR ORAL OR RECTAL ADMINISTRATION

Each 15 mL of syrup contains 10 g lactulose

Caution: Federal law prohibits dispensing without prescription

5. Mr. Ngo has been instructed to take Pepto-Bismol for his traveler's diarrhea. What is the generic name for Pepto-Bismol?

_____

6. Mrs. Anderson, a patient with hepatitis C, brings the following prescription to your pharmacy:

℞   Copegus 600 mg PO bid

_____

a. If the tablets are 200 mg, how many tablets will she receive in one day?

_____

7. Mr. Doole requires ranitidine in his total parenteral nutrition (TPN) for stress ulcer prophylaxis. The recommended dose is 150 mg/day. How many milliliters of Zantac for injection would Mr. Doole get in each TPN?

_____

NDC 0000-0000-00

ranitidine hydrochloride Injection

25 mg/mL*

40-mL Pharmacy Bulk Package — Not for Direct Infusion

Sterile   ℞ only

Contents should be used as soon as possible following initial closure puncture. Discard any unused portion within 24 hours of first entry.

* Each 1 mL of aqueous solution contains ranitidine 25 mg (as the hydrochloride); phenol 5 mg as preservative; monobasic potassium phosphate and dibasic sodium phosphate as buffers.

See package insert for Dosage and Administration and directions for use of Pharmacy Bulk Package.

Store between 4° and 25°C (39° and 77°F); excursions permitted to 30°C (86°F). Protect from light. Store vial in carton until time of use.

Understanding the Larger Medical Context

8. Ms. Copeland is 28 years old, 168 cm tall, and 170 lb. Would she qualify for Xenical therapy? Explain your answer.

     _____

     _____

9. To increase the chances for successful treatment of hepatitis C, which medication must be used with Copegus? Why?

     _____

10. Which medication can treat both diarrhea and constipation?

     _____

11. What is the prototype for stool softeners?

     _____

12. Which class of antiemetics is used for treatment of emesis in chemotherapy?

     _____

13. Give two examples of medications from the above class (question 12).

     _____

14. How often must a female patient be tested for pregnancy if prescribed bocepivir (Victrelis) or telaprevir (Incivek)?

     _____

Dispensing and Storing Drugs

15. The pharmacist is pregnant. An order comes down for Cytotec. Who should fill the script, and why?

     _____

16. Which two diet pills are C-IIs?

     _____

17. Which diet pill is OTC?

     _____

18. The technician dispensed Bactrim DS. This drug is a tablet. What must be done to the tray after the drug is counted out? Why?

     _____

19. Which weight loss drugs require a medication guide?

     _____

Putting Safety First

20. The patient is taking a trip to Africa. The prescriber wrote a script for Malarone. The patient states that she is going to take the drug as soon as the plane lands. She is going to be in Africa for seven days. The prescriber wrote for #16. When did the prescriber intend for the patient to start taking this drug? When does the prescriber intend for the patient to stop taking the drug?

21. Which antidiarrheals are C-IVs?

22. Which antidiarrheal is stored in the OTC area of the store?

Do the doses match the medications? If not, give a common dose.

23. Carafate is dosed every eight hours.

24. Rowasa 1 tab daily for Crohn disease

25. Lomotil combination of 0.25 mg diphenoxylate and 0.25 mg atropine

26. A BMI of at least 25 is required to initiate treatment with Xenical.

27. Malarone should be taken three to four days before entering the malaria area.

Understanding Concepts

28. _____ is a proton pump inhibitor that has an IV form.

29. MOM is the acronym for _____.

30. A BMI of at least 30 is required to initiate treatment of _____.

31. A _____ is a combination of bismuth subcitrate potassium, metronidazole, and tetracycline.

32. _____ forms a protective coat or shield over the ulcer; and is dosed every six hours.

33. Tonic water contains small amounts of _____, a drug used to treat malaria.

34. List the serotonin receptor antagonists designed to treat nausea induced by chemotherapy: _____

35. _____ is the brand name of sodium phosphate used as a bowel evacuant.

36. _____ is a proton pump inhibitor that comes in capsule form, and can be opened and mixed with apple sauce for those patients who have difficulty swallowing.

37. _____ is a monoclonal antibody used in the treatment of Crohn's disease.

38. The _____ is an index used to determine if one is obese.

39. A duodenal _____ is a peptic lesion.

40. _____ is the drug indicated for the treatment of infectious diarrhea caused by a waterborne protozoan.

41. _____ is a combination of calcium carbonate and simethicone.

42. _____ is a schedule IV drug used to treat obesity.

43. Most antacids are found in the _____ aisle of the pharmacy.

44. _____ is an anti-inflammatory medication used to treat Crohn's disease and ulcerative colitis.

45. _____ (trimethobenzamide) is used to treat worms.

46. _____ is the notation used for immune globulin that is administered IV.

47. _____ is the abbreviation of a condition characterized by a backflow of stomach acid.

Matching–Brand and Generic Drug Names

_____ 48. famotidine

_____ 49. omeprazole

_____ 50. cimetidine

_____ 51. sucralfate

_____ 52. ursodiol

_____ 53. metoclopramide

_____ 54. nitazoxanide

_____ 55. bisacodyl

_____ 56. lactulose

_____ 57. docusate

_____ 58. meclizine

a. Prilosec

b. Pepcid

c. Carafate

d. Tagamet

e. Antivert

f. Colace

g. Reglan

h. Actigall

i. Alinia

j. Enulose

k. Dulcolax

Matching–Terms and Definitions

_____ 59. antiemetic

_____ 60. body mass index (BMI)

_____ 61. chemoreceptor trigger zone (CTZ)

_____ 62. empty stomach

_____ 63. gastroesophageal reflux disease (GERD)

_____ 64. H₂ histamine receptor antagonist

_____ 65. Hepatitis

_____ 66. IVIG

_____ 67. morbid obesity

_____ 68. osmotic laxative

_____ 69. phenothiazine

_____ 70. proton pump inhibitor

_____ 71. reflux

_____ 72. saline laxative

_____ 73. surfactant laxative

_____ 74. traveler's diarrhea

_____ 75. vertigo

a. A disease of the liver that causes inflammation, can be acute or chronic, and has several forms A through G

b. A drug, related to the typical antipsychotics, that controls vomiting by inhibiting the CTZ

c. A drug that blocks gastric acid secretion by inhibiting the enzyme that pumps hydrogen ions into the stomach

d. A drug that controls nausea and vomiting

e. A GI disease characterized by radiating burning or pain in the chest and an acid taste, caused by backflow of acidic stomach contents across an incompetent lower esophageal sphincter; also referred to as heartburn

f. A guide to use in determining whether to initiate pharmacologic treatment for obesity; calculated by dividing the patient's weight (in kilograms) by the patient's height (in meters) squared (kg/m^2)

g. A state in which an individual's weight is two or more times the ideal body weight (IBW)

h. A stool softener that has a detergent activity that facilitates mixing of fat and water, making the stool soft and mushy

i. An agent that blocks acid and pepsin secretion in response to histamine, gastrin, foods, distention, caffeine, or cholinergic stimulation; used to treat GERD and H. pylori

j. An area below the floor of the fourth ventricle of the brain that can trigger nausea and vomiting when certain signals are received

k. An inorganic salt that attracts water into the hollow portion (lumen) of the colon, increasing intraluminal pressure to cause evacuation

l. An organic substance that draws water into the colon and thereby stimulates evacuation

m. Backflow; specifically in GERD, the backflow of acidic stomach contents across an incompetent lower esophageal sphincter

n. Diarrhea caused by ingesting contaminated food or water; so called because it is often contracted by travelers in countries where the water supply is contaminated

o. The notation for immune globulin that is given intravenously

p. The sensation of the room spinning when one gets up or changes positions; can be treated with anticholinergic agents

q. 2 hours before or after eating

Renal System Drugs

11

Reading Drug Labels and Medication Orders

1. You receive the following prescription, and the product available in the pharmacy is 5 mg/mL of oral liquid in a 473 mL container:

   ℞   Ditropan Syrup 7 mg bid

   a. How much do you need to dispense for a 30 day supply?

   b. If you dispensed the entire bottle, how long would it last the patient?

2. You receive the following prescription, and the drug label shown is the product available in the pharmacy.

   ℞   Tolterodine LA cap 2 mg every day #30

℞ only	NDC 0000-0000-00
See package insert for complete product information.	
Dispense in tight container.	*tolterodine tartrate tablets*
Store at controlled room temperature 20° to 25°C (68° to 77°F) [see USP].	**2 mg** ☙ 817373406 LOT S L EXP
	60 Tablets

a. Will a capsule or tablet be dispensed?

_____

b. How many will be dispensed for a 90 day supply?

_____

c. How many bottles will be needed?

_____

d. Where is this bottle stored?

_____

3. You receive the following prescription for a product available in the pharmacy:

R̥   Lupron Depot 3 as directed

a. How will this product be administered?

_____

b. How long will this dose last?

_____

4. You receive the following prescription, and the product available in the pharmacy is available as 40 mg/mL in a 240 mL container:

R̥   Megace Susp 60 mg bid

How long will this bottle last the patient?

_____

5. You receive the following prescription:

R̥   Torsemide 20 mg IV every day

The pharmacy has a 2 mL and a 5 mL size of 10 mg/mL. Which of the two products do you choose to fill the prescription? Why?

_____

_____

Understanding the Larger Medical Context

6. Which bacteria causes most urinary tract infections?

   _____

7. What are side effects of potassium-sparing diuretics?

   _____

8. What are the stages of renal disease?

   _____

   _____

   _____

   _____

9. By which three processes do the kidneys produce urine?

   _____

   _____

   _____

10. What are five symptoms of chronic renal insufficiency?

    _____

    _____

    _____

Dispensing and Storing Drugs

11. The prescriber wants an osmotic IV diuretic. Which one will the technician mix?

    _____

12. The IV form of Cellcept can only be mixed with which diluent?

    _____

Indicate which drugs have black box warnings (BBW), medication guides (MG), both (B), or neither (N).

13. Aranesp _____

14. ciprofloxacin _____

15. hydrochlorothiazide _____

16. Oxytrol _____

17. nitrofurantoin _____

18. Uroxatral _____

19. doxazosin _____

20. phenazopyridine _____

21. Epogen _____

22. CellCept _____

23. mannitol _____

24. Nephrocaps is a brand of vitamins specially formulated for dialysis patients. What is in Nephrocaps?

_____

25. What is the third most common cause of renal failure in hospitalized patients?

_____

26. Which drugs can cause aluminum toxicity in patients on dialysis?

_____

27. Which drug is oral therapy for interstitial cystitis?

_____

28. Which drug has a local anesthetic effect in the urinary tract?

_____

29. Which alpha-1 blocker is more selective: Flomax (tamsulosin) or Hytrin (terrazosin)?

_____

30. Which drugs are urinary antispasmodics that decrease urinary frequency?

_____

31. Where in the kidney does each of the following types of medication work?

thiazide diuretics
loop diuretics
carbonic anhydrase inhibitors
osmotic diuretics

a. distal tubule   _____
b. glomerulus   _____
c. loop of Henle   _____
d. proximal tubule   _____

Putting Safety First

32. Why is it important to check the labs of patients on furosemide to see if their potassium levels are appropriate?

_____

33. List three drug classes that should be avoided in BPH patients.

_____

34. HCTZ is an abbreviation for what drug?

_____

35. What is the purpose of adding triamterene to hydrochlorothiazide?

_____

36. Name two brand names for the combination triamterene-hydrochlorothiazide.

_____

37. _____ is a class of drugs is used to decrease high blood pressure and treat BPH.

38. _____ is a potassium sparing diuretic that is 100 times more specific in its affinity for aldosterone than spironolactone.

39. _____ is voiding 8 or more times in 24 hours.

40. _____ is an urinary analgesic that colors the urine orange and stains anything it contacts.

41. _____ is a drug used to treat both urinary problems and depression.

42. _____ is the abbreviation for prostate gland enlargement.

43. _____ is the frequent need to urinate at night.

44. _____ is the working unit of the kidney.

45. _____ is the removal of substances from the blood during urine formation.

46. _____ is the abbreviation for end-stage renal disease.

Matching–Brand and Generic Drug Names

_____ 47. Flomax

_____ 48. Esidrex

_____ 49. Hyzaar

_____ 50. Lasix

_____ 51. Lozol

_____ 52. Maxzide

_____ 53. Tenoretic

_____ 54. Zestoretic

_____ 55. Ziac

a. indapamide

b. atenolol-hydrochlorothiazide

c. bisoprolol-hydrochlorothiazide

d. furosemide

e. hydrochlorothiazide

f. lisinopril-hydrochlorothiazide

g. losartan-hydrochlorothiazide

h. triamterene-hydrochlorothiazide

i. tamsulosin

Matching–Terms and Definitions

_____ 56. carbonic anhydrase inhibitor

_____ 57. diuretic

_____ 58. hematocrit

_____ 59. loop diuretic

_____ 60. nocturia

_____ 61. osmotic diuretic

_____ 62. potassium sparing diuretic

_____ 63. reabsorption

_____ 64. thiazide diuretic

_____ 65. urinary tract infection (UTI)

a. A diuretic that acts in the proximal tubule to increase urine volume and change the pH to alkaline

b. A drug based on benzothiadiazine that blocks a pump that removes sodium and chloride together from the distal tubule

c. A drug that increases the osmotic pressure of glomerular filtrate, thereby inhibiting tubular reabsorption of water and electrolytes and increasing urinary output

d. A drug that inhibits reabsorption of sodium and chloride in the loop of Henle, thereby causing increased urinary output

e. A drug that promotes excretion of water and sodium but inhibits the exchange of sodium for potassium

f. A substance that rids the body of excess fluid and electrolytes by increasing the urine output

g. An infection caused by bacteria, usually _E. coli_, that enter via the urethra and progress up the urinary tract; characterized by the presence of bacteria in the urine with localized symptoms

h. The process by which substances are pulled back into the blood after waste products have been removed during the formation of urine

i. The proportion of volume of red blood cells to the total volume of blood

j. Urinary frequency at night

Drugs for Cardiovascular Diseases

12

Reading Drug Labels and Medication Orders

1. You receive the following prescription, and the drug label shown is the product you pick up from the pharmacy shelf:

   ℞   Catapres patch 0.2 mg q7 d

NDC 0000-0000-00	Transdermal use only

   CLONIDINE

   Transdermal Therapeutic System

   4 patches and 4 adhesive covers

   Delivery of 0.2 mg clondine per day for one week.

   Caution: Federal law prohibits
   dispensing without prescription

   a. How many 0.2 mg patches will the patient receive for a one-month supply? Show your calculations.

   _____

   b. A box of Catapres has been opened. You want to confirm that no contents have been removed. What comes in a box of Catapres?

   _____

   _____

2. You receive the following prescription, and the available drug contains 4 g of resin in 9 g of powder:

   ℞   cholestyramine 1 packet PO tid

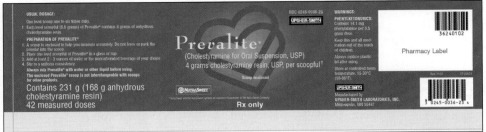

a. How many grams would the patient receive in one day?

_____

b. How should this product be prepared before administration?

_____

3. You receive the following order, and the drug label shown is the product you pick up from the pharmacy shelf:

℞ Amiodarone 900 mg/500 ml IV per atrial arrhythmia protocol

How many milliliters of amiodarone would you require to make this product?

_____

_____

| NDC 0000-0000-00 |
| For IV use only |
| **AMIODARONE HCL INJECTION** |
| 900 mg/18 mL |
| 50 mg/mL |
| Caution: Federal law prohibits dispensing without prescription |

Store at room temperature, 15° to 25°C (59° to 77°F).

4. You receive the following order:

℞ Metoprolol 400 mg PO daily

What is the brand name for the product you will dispense?

_____

5. You receive the following prescription:

℞ Hyzaar 50/12.5 1 tab PO daily

a. What are the generic ingredients in this product?

_____

b. How many milligrams of diuretic will the patient receive in one month?

_____

6. You receive the following prescription, and the drug is available as a 20 mg/mL injection:

> ℞ hydralazine 20 mg IV q6 h

The hospital requires a five-day supply to be stored in an automated dispensing machine on the floor. How many vials would you send to the floor? Show your calculations.

_____

_____

7. You receive the following prescription:

> ℞ Lovenox (enoxaparin) 90 mg SC bid

Lovenox comes in the following syringes: 60 mg/0.6 mL, 80 mg/0.8 mL, 100 mg/mL, and 120 mg/0.8 mL

a. Which product would you select to fill this prescription?

_____

b. How many milliliters would correspond to the 90 mg dose?

_____

8. You receive the following prescription:

> ℞ aspirin EC 325 mg PO daily

a. What does EC stand for?

_____

b. How would this differ from a prescription for baby aspirin?

_____

9. You are assembling some pharmacy kits for the intensive care units at your hospital. The kit contains:

> #1 125 mg vial of diltiazem for injection
>
> #1 100 mL bag of sodium chloride

a. If these two products were added together, what would the resultant concentration be?

_____

b. Where would this kit be stored?

_____

Understanding the Larger Medical Context

10. What does ACE and ARB stand for? In what ways is an ACE and an ARB different?

_____

_____

_____

_____

11. What is the first drug approved for a specific race, and which race?

_____

12. Why is Coreg given with food?

_____

13. Describe the ideal blood cholesterol level per 100 mL of blood.

_____

_____

14. How is nebivelol (Bystolic) different from other beta blockers?

_____

_____

15. Which lipoproteins are "good" cholesterol?

_____

16. Which lipoproteins are "bad" cholesterol?

_____

17. Why is it difficult to determine which size to dispense of the low-molecular-weight heparins? What should a pharmacy technician do before the product is dispensed?

_____

_____

_____

_____

_____

18. The pharmacist suspects that a patient is having a heart attack and tells you to quickly get an aspirin. Would you get an 81 mg or a 325 mg aspirin? Would you get an enteric coated aspirin or a plain aspirin, and why?

_____

_____

19. Manufacturers are combining more than one drug into a tablet, especially heart and cholesterol medications. What are two reasons for combining drugs?

_____

Dispensing and Storing Drugs

Mark whether or not each of the following drugs must be dispensed in its original container.

20. Aggrenox   yes _____   no _____

21. Nitro Stat   yes _____   no _____

22. Plavix   yes _____   no _____

23. Edarbi   yes _____   no _____

24. phenytoin   yes _____   no _____

25. Nitro Dur   yes _____   no _____

26. Catepres patch   yes _____   no _____

27. digoxin tablets   yes _____   no _____

28. Lovenox syringes   yes _____   no _____

29. Cardura tablets   yes _____   no _____

30. Lipitor tablets   yes _____   no _____

31. nifedipine XL   yes _____   no _____

32. Tekturna   yes _____   no _____

33. TriCor   yes _____   no _____

34. warfarin   yes _____   no _____

Which drugs have a black box warning (BBW), require a medication guide (MG), both (B), or neither (N)?

35. nadolol _____

36. Norvasc _____

37. amiodarone _____

38. Tikosyn _____

39. Multaq _____

40. digoxin _____

41. Lovenox _____

42. Asclera _____

43. Xarelto _____

44. Trilipix _____

45. Questran _____

46. Dilantin _____

47. aspirin _____

48. Coumadin _____

49. Valsartan _____

50. minoxidil _____

51. heparin _____

52. dabigtran _____

53. Crestor _____

54. dipyridamole _____

Putting Safety First

55. Which anticoagulants must have medication guides?

_____

56. Which vasodilators have black box warnings?

_____

57. Which cholesterol medication has a medication guide?

_____

Does the dose match the medication? If not, give a common dose.

58. Viagra 15 mg

_____

59. reteplase given in one injection of 20 mL

_____

Understanding Concepts

60. A clonidine patch should be worn for _____.

61. _____ is a fibrinolytic agent given in two injections of 10 mL separated by an interval of 30 minutes.

62. _____ is a membrane stabilizing agent that is also an anticonvulsant.

63. Dalteparin is an example of a low-molecular weight _____.

64. _____ pectoris is chest pain.

65. _____ is a waxlike constituent of animal origin that is important in discussion of circulatory health.

66. _____ stands for myocardial infarction, or heart attack.

67. _____ are a type of fat molecules that release fatty acids into the blood.

68. CHF stands for _____.

69. An _____ is a variation from normal heart beat.

70. _____ is a slow heart rate.

71. _____ blood pressure is blood pressure during heart dilation.

72. A _____ is clotting within a blood vessel.

73. _____ is a vasodilator approved for erectile dysfunction.

74. List the advantages of LMWHs over heparin.

_____

_____

_____

_____

Matching–Drug Names and Drug Groups

_____ 75. alfuzosin

_____ 76. amlodipine-atorvastatin

_____ 77. amlodipine-benazepril

_____ 78. amlodipine-valsartan

_____ 79. aspirin

_____ 80. aspirin-dipyridamole

_____ 81. atorvastatin

_____ 82. benazepril-hydrochlorothiazide

_____ 83. carvedilol

_____ 84. clonidine

_____ 85. clopidogrel

_____ 86. diltiazem

_____ 87. digoxin

_____ 88. ezetimibe

_____ 89. irbesartan

_____ 90. irbesartan-hydrochlorothiazide

_____ 91. losartan

_____ 92. losartan-hydrochlorothiazide

_____ 93. nisoldipine

_____ 94. olmesartan

_____ 95. phenytoin

_____ 96. pravastatin

_____ 97. propranolol

_____ 98. ramipril

_____ 99. rosuvastatin

_____ 100. sildenafil

_____ 101. simvastatin

_____ 102. telmisartan

_____ 103. trandolapril-verapamil

_____ 104. valsartan

_____ 105. valsartan-hydrochlorothiazide

_____ 106. warfarin

a. Aggrenox

b. Altace

c. Avalide

d. Avapro

e. Benicar

f. Caduet

g. Cardizem

h. Catapres

i. Coreg

j. Coumadin

k. Cozaar

l. Crestor

m. Dilantin

n. Diovan

o. Diovan HCT

p. Exforge

q. Hyzaar

r. Inderal

s. Lanoxin

t. Lipitor

u. Lotensin HCT

v. Lotrel

w. Micardis

x. Plavix

y. Pravachol

z. many names

aa. Sular

bb. Tarka

cc. Uroaxtral

dd. Viagra

ee. Zetia

ff. Zocor

Matching–Terms and Definitions

_____ 107. angina pectoris

_____ 108. anticoagulant

_____ 109. antiplatelet

_____ 110. arrhythmia

_____ 111. beta blocker

_____ 112. bradycardia

_____ 113. calcium channel blocker

_____ 114. clotting cascade

_____ 115. congestive heart failure (CHF)

_____ 116. fibrinolytic

_____ 117. high-density lipoproteins (HDLs)

_____ 118. hyperlipidemia

_____ 119. hypertension

_____ 120. International Normalized Ratio (INR)

_____ 121. low-density lipoproteins (LDLs)

_____ 122. membrane stabilizing agent

_____ 123. myocardial infarction (MI)

_____ 124. partial thromboplastin time (PTT)

_____ 125. statin

_____ 126. stroke

_____ 127. tachycardia

_____ 128. thrombus

_____ 129. thrombocytopenia

_____ 130. transient ischemic attack (TIA)

a. A Class I antiarrhythmic drug that slows the movement of ions into cardiac cells, thus reducing the action potential and dampening abnormal rhythms and heartbeats

b. A Class II antiarrhythmic drug that competitively blocks response to beta adrenergic stimulation and therefore lowers heart rate, myocardial contractility, blood pressure, and myocardial oxygen demand; used to treat arrhythmias, MIs, and angina

c. A Class IV antiarrhythmic drug that prevents the movement of calcium ions through slow channels; used for most supraventricular tachyarrhythmias and in angina

d. A condition in which the heart can no longer pump adequate blood to the body's tissues; results in engorgement of the pulmonary vessels

e. A decrease in the bone marrow production of blood platelets

f. A drug that prevents clot formation by affecting clotting factors

g. A drug that reduces the risk of clot formation by inhibiting platelet aggregation

h. A heart attack occurs when a region of the heart muscle is deprived of oxygen

i. A method of standardizing the prothrombin time (PT) by comparing it to a standard index

j. A series of events that initiate blood clotting, or coagulation

k. A test that measures the function of the intrinsic and common pathways in blood clotting; affected by heparin

l. Abnormally slow heart rate (below 60 beats per minute)

m. An agent that dissolves clots

n. An HMG-CoA reductase inhibitor, a drug that inhibits the rate-limiting step in cholesterol formation

o. Any variation from the normal heartbeat

p. Blood clot

q. Elevated blood pressure, where systolic blood pressure is greater than 140 mm Hg and diastolic pressure is greater than 90 mm Hg

r. Elevation of the levels of one or more of the lipoproteins in the blood

s. Excessively fast heart rate

t. Lipoproteins containing 5% triglyceride, 25% cholesterol, and 50% protein; "good cholesterol"

Definitions continued next page

u. Lipoproteins containing 6% triglycerides and 65% cholesterol; "bad cholesterol"

v. The result of an event (finite, ongoing, or protracted occurrences) that interrupts oxygen supply to an area of the brain; usually caused by cerebral infarction or cerebral hemorrhage

w. Spasmodic or suffocating chest pain caused by an imbalance between oxygen supply and oxygen demand

x. Temporary neurologic change that occurs when part of the brain lacks sufficient blood supply over a brief period of time; may be a warning sign and predictor of imminent stroke

Drugs for Muscle and Joint Disease and Pain

13

Reading Drug and Medication Orders

1. You receive the following prescription, and the drug label shown is the product you pick up from the pharmacy shelf:

   ℞ Mobic 7.5 mg #60 bid

   > NDC 0000-0000-00
   > **MELOXICAM**
   > **15 mg tablets**
   > *100 tablets*
   > R_x only

   a. Is a medication guide required when the prescription is dispensed to the patient? Explain your answer.

   _____

   b. What auxiliary label would you put on the medication?

   _____

2. You receive the following prescription:

   ℞ Enbrel 50 mg SC weekly

   a. What is the drug class of Enbrel?

   _____

   b. When would a physician prescribe Enbrel for a patient?

   _____

   _____

3. You receive the following prescription:

   ℞ Ibuprofen 200 mg I-IV daily prn

a. Is this prescription Rx or OTC?

_____

b. What is the maximum daily dose of ibuprofen?

_____

4. What is the maximum daily dose of acetaminophen?

_____

5. The technician receives this prescription:

   ℞   Percocet 7.5/500 1-2 q4h # 120

   Is it safe to dispense this prescription? Why or why not?

   _____

   _____

Understanding the Larger Medical Context

6. What is a muscle, and what is a joint?

   _____

   _____

7. What are the advantages of using nonnarcotic analgesics compared to narcotic analgesics?

   _____

   _____

   _____

8. What is a muscle relaxant, and what are the possible side effects of taking a muscle relaxant?

   _____

   _____

9. In what ways is osteoarthritis different from rheumatoid arthritis?

   _____

   _____

   _____

10. What role do cyclooxygenase-1 and cyclooxygenase-2 play in pain and inflammation?

   _____

   _____

11. How do nonsteroidal anti-inflammatory agents work?

_____

_____

_____

12. Why are opiates combined with NSAIDs?

_____

_____

_____

13. What are advantages and disadvantages of using DMARDs?

_____

_____

_____

14. What is gout, and how does it affect the body?

_____

_____

_____

_____

15. What is the most common effect of NSAIDs, and how is it minimized?

_____

_____

16. What is a mixed analgesic?

_____

17. What is the antidote for acetaminophen?

_____

18. Which drug is a controlled substance in some states, but not all, and binds to opiate receptors?

_____

19. What is the only COX-2 still on the market?

_____

20. List five tips for patients using an NSAID.

_____

_____

_____

21. Which NSAIDs have parenteral forms?

_____

22. Which NSAIDs are available OTC?

_____

Dispensing and Storing Drugs

23. What auxiliary label would you put on all of the NSAIDs?

_____

24. Should any of the drugs in this chapter be dispensed in the original containers? If so, which ones?

_____

_____

_____

25. Which class of drugs discussed in this chapter must have a medication guide?

_____

26. Which muscle relaxant has a black box warning?

_____

27. There is one class of drugs in this chapter for which every drug has a medication guide. Which class is it?

_____

_____

Putting Safety First

28. Which gout drugs must be dispensed with a medication guide?

_____

29. Which antipyretic/analgesic is safe for pregnant women?

_____

30. What is the maximum asprin dose for an adult?

_____

31. Why must the prescriber be notified if a patient brings in a prescription for Tylenol with a dosage of more than 4 grams per day?

_____

_____

Understanding Concepts

32. _____ is a drug approved for Crohn's disease that has also been approved for rheumatoid arthritis.

33. _____ is the only NSAID available as a suppository.

34. _____ is a muscle relaxant and a controlled substance; it is also a benzodiazepine.

35. _____ is the safest NSAID for cardiovascular events.

36. _____ is an effective analgesic and antipyretic; it is a first-line medication for mild to moderate pain and is safe in pregnancy.

37. Allopurinol and colchicine are prescribed to treat _____.

38. _____ is an NSAID that comes in patch form.

39. _____ was the first OTC analgesic for children since acetaminophen.

40. _____ is the brand name for the Cox-2 inhibitor.

41. _____ is a combination of tramadol and acetaminophen.

42. _____ and _____ are both brand names for ibuprofen.

43. _____ is a word for low blood pressure.

44. _____ is a word for high blood pressure.

45. _____ is tramadol and ibuprofen.

46. ACh is the abbreviation for _____, a neurotransmitter important in muscle contraction.

47. _____ are a group of drugs important in the treatment of rheumatoid arthritis.

48. _____ arthritis is an autoimmune disease.

49. _____ syndrome is a condition most common in children exposed to chicken pox.

50. _____ is the abbreviation of a group of drugs used for treatment of arthritis.

51. _____ pain originates in the organs and is sharp and stabbing.

52. _____ is a deposit of sodium urate at the joint.

53. _____ pain is dull and throbbing and originates from skin, muscle, or bone.

54. _____ is inflammation of the joints.

55. _____ is a painful condition in which muscles are in a state of continuous contraction.

56. _____ arthritis is the result of improper excretion of uric acid.

Matching–Drug Names and Drug Groups

_____ 57. acetaminophen

_____ 58. allopurinol

_____ 59. carisoprodol

_____ 60. celecoxib

_____ 61. cyclobenzaprine

_____ 62. diclofenac

_____ 63. esomeprazole-naproxen

_____ 64. ibuprofen

_____ 65. meloxicam

_____ 66. metaxalone

_____ 67. naproxen

a. Aleve

b. Celebrex

c. Flexeril

d. Mobic

e. Motrin

f. Skelaxin

g. Soma

h. Tylenol

i. Vimovo

j. Voltaren

k. Zyloprim

Matching–Terms and Definitions

_____ 68. analgesic

_____ 69. antipyretic

_____ 70. APAP

_____ 71. arthritis

_____ 72. ASA

_____ 73. autoimmune disease

_____ 74. Celebrex

_____ 75. cyclooxygenase-2 (COX-2)

_____ 76. disease-modifying antirheumatic drugs (DMARDs)

_____ 77. gouty arthritis

_____ 78. muscle relaxant

_____ 79. muscle spasticity

_____ 80. nonnarcotic analgesic

_____ 81. nonsteroidal anti-inflammatory drugs (NSAIDs)

_____ 82. osteoarthritis

_____ 83. rheumatoid arthritis

_____ 84. salicylates

_____ 85. SLE

a. A class of nonnarcotic analgesics that have both pain-relieving and antipyretic (fever reducing) properties

b. Degenerative joint disease resulting in loss of cartilage, elasticity, and thickness

c. An autoimmune disease in which the body's immune system attacks its own connective tissue; characterized by inflammation of the synovial membrane of the joints

d. A condition whereby muscle fibers are in a state of involuntary, continuous contraction that causes pain

e. A disease resulting from the improper excretion of uric acid; also called gout

f. A drug that reduces or prevents skeletal muscle contraction

g. A drug used for pain, inflammation, and fever that is not a controlled substance

h. An enzyme that is present in the synovial fluid of arthritis patients and is associated with the pain and inflammation of arthritis

i. Agents that can modify the progression of rheumatoid arthritis

j. Fever reducing

k. Illness in which the immune system attacks and destroys healthy tissue within the body

l. Joint inflammation; persistent pain due to functional problems of the joints

m. Anti-inflammatory, analgesic, and antipyretic drugs that are not controlled substances or steroids; used to treat arthritis and for other indications such as pain and inflammation

n. Pain relieving

o. aspirin

p. acetaminophen

q. Systemic Lupus Erythematosus

r. only Cox-2 inhibitor on market

Hormonal Disorders and Their Treatment

Reading Drug Labels and Medication Orders

1. You receive the following prescription, and the drug label shown is the product you pick up from the pharmacy shelf:

℞   Medrol dose pack #1 as directed

```
NDC 0000-0000-00
21 Tablets
6505-01-131-5619
```

methylprednisolone tablets, USP

4 mg
Unit of Use

℞ only

See package insert for complete product information.

Keep patient under close observation of a physician.
Store at controlled room temperature
20° to 25°C (68° to 77°F) [see USP].

The prescriber writes TUD. What does TUD mean, and why is Medrol prescribed this way?

_____

_____

_____

_____

2. You receive the following prescription, and the drug label shown is the product you pick up from the pharmacy shelf:

℞   Synthroid 0.05 mg 1 tbsp every day

What does DAW mean? Why will the prescriber often write DAW for Synthroid?

_____

_____

_____

_____

NDC 0000-0000-00

LEVOTHYROXINE SODIUM TABLETS, USP

50 mcg (0.05 mg)

100 TABLETS

Caution: Federal law prohibits dispensing without prescription

3. You receive the following prescription, and the drug label shown is the product you pick up from the pharmacy shelf:

℞   Glucotrol 10 mg bid #60 RF × 5

a. Does the drug label correspond to the product indicated in the prescription? Explain your answer.

_____

_____

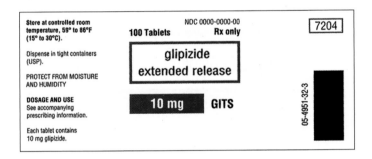

b. What is the drug class of Glucotrol, and for what medical condition is Glucotrol typically used? Explain the response the body has to Glucotrol.

_____

_____

c. What are the side effects of Glucotrol?

_____

_____

_____

4. You receive the following prescription for a 14-year-old patient who weighs exactly 44 kg. The drug label shown is the product to be dispensed, and you are to dispense the 12 mg cartridge.

℞ Humatrope 0.35 mg/kg weekly, given in daily SC INJ

a. What is the total weekly dose? Show your calculations.

_____

_____

b. What is the daily dose? Show your calculations.

_____

_____

REFRIGERATE   NDC 0000-0000-00
AVOID FREEZING   VL7555
Rx only   YL 0350 FSAMX

12 mg

somatropin [rDNA origin] for injection

c. If the strength is 4 mg/mL, what is the daily volume of injection? Show your calculations.

_____

_____

d. How are Humatrope cartridges stored?

_____

_____

Understanding the Larger Medical Context

5. Explain the importance of exercising caution when using beta blockers in diabetic patients. Then list five signs and symptoms of hypoglycemia.

_____

_____

_____

_____

_____

_____

_____

6. Name the four types of diabetes and identify the characteristics of each type.

_____

_____

_____

_____

_____

_____

_____

_____

7. What can cause cretinism? What are the signs and symptoms of cretinism?

_____

_____

_____

_____

8. What are some causes of male impotence that are not related to medication?

_____

_____

9. What causes menopause to occur? When does menopause begin for women? What are common symptoms experienced by women during menopause?

_____

_____

_____

_____

10. What might cause a potential false-negative and a potential false-positive in a home pregnancy test?

_____

_____

_____

_____

11. In what ways are osteoclasts and osteoblasts different?

_____

_____

_____

12. What is the main reason for using corticosteroids? Why are corticosteroids prescribed?

_____

_____

_____

13. No oral insulin preparations exist. Why?

_____

_____

14. What are the signs and symptoms of hyperthyroidism?

_____

_____

_____

_____

Dispensing and Storing Drugs

Where would the following medications be stored in the pharmacy?

15. Lantus

_____

16. teriparatide

_____

17. Femring

_____

18. Synthroid

_____

19. Byetta

_____

Which of these drugs must have a medication guide?

20. Fosamax 10 mg   yes _____   no _____

21. Synthroid   yes _____   no _____

22. AndroGel   yes _____   no _____

23. Flagyl   yes _____   no _____

24. Why is it important that women on birth control pills not smoke?

_____

_____

_____

25. What is the drug schedule of testosterone substances?

_____

26. What does DAW mean?

_____

_____

27. Why is it important to make sure the pharmacist counsels the patient when he or she gets a steroid dose pack? Can the technician counsel the patient if the pharmacist is busy?

_____

_____

_____

Putting Safety First

28. Which drug for male impotence requires a medication guide?

_____

29. Which antibiotic used for sexually transmitted diseases has a black box warning?

_____

30. Femring is supplied on a ring inserted into the vagina for how long?

_____

31. How often is alendronate dosed?

_____

32. What is a maximum dose of Zometa? Over what time period should it be administered?

_____

Understanding Concepts

33. _____ is a biguanide oral hypoglycemic agent.

34. _____ is an agent used for diabetic ulcers.

35. _____ is a generic drug indicated for the treatment and prevention of osteoporosis in post-menopausal women and in Paget's bone disease for both men and women.

36. _____ is the rapid-acting insulin that may be used with the pump.

37. _____ is a male hormone that is manufactured as a buccal system.

38. _____ is referred to as the "weekender" because it is effective for 36 hours.

39. _____ was the first oral therapy for impotence.

40. _____ generics are the actual brand name oral contraceptives relabeled and marketed under a generic product name, not listed in the orange book.

41. _____ is conjugated estrogen made from a pregnant mare's urine.

42. _____ is a combination of glyburide and metformin.

43. Women who are taking biphosphanates for bone loss should also be taking calcium and _____.

44. Technicians must make sure the pharmacist counsels anyone taking birth control pills and an _____, because the birth control pill becomes less effective when that drug is added.

45. _____ is a combination of ethinyl estradiol and drospirenone.

46. An _____ is a cell that forms bone.

47. _____ is the gland that produces hormones that stimulate various body tissues.

48. _____ is the practice of taking OCs on three 21-day cycles without a pill-free interval.

49. _____ stands for pelvic inflammatory disease.

50. A woman taking Seasonale will have _____ menstrual cycle(s) yearly.

51. List the benefits of tri-cycling: _____

_____

52. List two reasons for hormone replacement in menopausal women: _____

_____

Matching–Drug Names and Drug Groups

_____ 53. alendronate

_____ 54. conjugated estrogen

_____ 55. estradiol

_____ 56. estradiol-levonorgestrel

_____ 57. ethinyl estradiol-levonorgestrel

_____ 58. ethinyl estradiol–norgestimate

_____ 59. ethinyl estradiol-norelgestromin

_____ 60. glimepiride

_____ 61. glipizide

_____ 62. glyburide

_____ 63. insulin glargine

_____ 64. insulin lispro

_____ 65. levothyroxine

_____ 66. methylprednisolone

_____ 67. risedronate

_____ 68. sildenafil

_____ 69. tadalafil

a. Actonel

b. Amaryl

c. Aviane

d. Cialis

e. Climara Pro

f. Fosamax

g. Glucotrol

h. Humalog

i. Lantus

j. Micronase

k. Ortho Evra

l. Ortho Tri-Cyclen

m. Premarin

n. Solu-Medrol

o. Synthroid

p. Viagra

q. Vivelle Dot

Matching–Terms and Definitions

_____ 70. AB rated

_____ 71. DAW

_____ 72. estrogen

_____ 73. gestational diabetes

_____ 74. glucocorticoid

_____ 75. HbA1C

_____ 76. impotence

_____ 77. oral contraceptive (OCs)

_____ 78. osteoporosis

_____ 79. progesterone

_____ 80. testosterone

_____ 81. virilization

a. A combination of one or more hormonal compounds taken orally to prevent the occurrence of pregnancy

b. A hormone that is responsible for sperm production, sexual potency, and the maintenance of muscle mass and strength, among other functions

c. Corticosteroid involved in metabolism and immune system regulation

d. Diabetes that occurs during pregnancy when insufficient insulin is produced

e. Failure of the male to initiate or to maintain an erection until ejaculation

f. Glycosylated hemoglobin; an "average" of the sugar measured in blood glucose over a period of time

g. Instruction in a prescription to prevent substitution of generic drugs for the branded drug

h. Refers to a generic drug rated as bioequivalent to the branded drug by the FDA as shown by an experimental study

i. One of the group of hormones that stimulate the growth of reproductive tissue in females

j. The condition of reduced bone mineral density, disrupted microarchitecture of bone structure, and increased likelihood of fracture

k. The development of male characteristics

l. The hormone that prepares the uterus for the reception and development of the fertilized ovum

Topical, Ophthalmic, and Otic Medications

15

Reading Drug Labels and Medication Orders

1. You receive the following prescription:

   ℞   tretinoin cream 0.05% apply daily for wrinkles

   a. You identify Retin-A cream 0.05% as the product available. Is this the correct product? Explain your answer.

   _____

   _____

   _____

   b. How does tretinoin work?

   _____

   _____

   _____

2. While you are working in the pharmacy, a physician calls and asks you to send Bactroban ointment for treating a patient with impetigo. The physician mentions that the patient has multiple lesions. You have Bactroban cream in the pharmacy. Would you send this product? Explain your answer.

   _____

   _____

   _____

   _____

   _____

3. A patient brings in the following prescription and asks how to use it:

> ℞ Cerumenex UAD may repeat x 1

What information should be provided to the patient?

_____

_____

_____

Understanding the Larger Medical Context

4. When treating skin ailments, can creams and ointments be interchanged? What could result if the medications were interchanged on a dermatologist's prescription? Would a dermatologist typically use a cream or an ointment to treat dry skin problems? What about wet skin problems?

_____

_____

_____

_____

_____

5. What is acne? What causes acne?

_____

_____

_____

6. Is it common practice for the physician to write a prescription for an ophthalmic agent to be used in the ear? Is it common practice for an otic agent to be used in the eye? Explain your answers.

_____

_____

_____

7. In what ways are open-angle glaucoma and narrow-angle glaucoma different? Which type of glaucoma is more common?

_____

_____

_____

_____

_____

8. As a pharmacy technician, what can you do to help patients prevent photosensitivity?

_____

_____

_____

_____

_____

9. A patient recently started lisinopril for her hypertension and developed sunburn while gardening outside. She wants your help in selecting a sunscreen because she does not understand what SPF, UV-A, or UV-B mean. How do you explain the differences among the notations?

_____

_____

_____

_____

_____

_____

_____

_____

10. Write instructions for applying erythromycin eye ointment in language a patient would understand.

_____

_____

_____

11. A patient has prescriptions for two different eyedrops and applies them four times daily. What must the patient be told about using these drops together?

_____

12. Are OTC medications to treat head lice as effective as a prescription medication? Explain your answer.

_____

_____

Dispensing and Storing Drugs

Which drugs require medication guides (MG), have black box warnings (BBW), both (B), or neither (N)?

13. Xalatan _____

14. dorzolamide _____

15. BenzaClin _____

16. erythromycin ophthalmic ointment _____

17. Vigamox _____

18. BenzaClin _____

19. Retin-A _____

20. Dovonex _____

21. Ciprodex _____

22. Ciloxan _____

Putting Safety First

Does the indication match the drug? If not, list what the drug is commonly used for.

23. pyrethrins for ringworm

_____

24. Botox for wrinkles

_____

25. benzoyl peroxide wash for sunburn

_____

26. tretinoin for wrinkles

_____

27. azelaic acid for acne

_____

28. Cerumenex for narrow-angle glaucoma

_____

29. tacrolimus for eczema

_____

30. imiquimod for ear infections

_____

31. eflornithine for dandruff

_____

32. fluorouracil for actinic keratosis

_____

Understanding Concepts

33. Patients on ventilators who have scheduled mouth cleansings throughout the day with _____ have decreased incidences of pneumonia.

34. _____ is used for unwanted facial hair.

35. _____ is an ophthalmic antifungal.

36. _____ is a combination of mequinol and tretinoin used for sun-damaged skin.

37. _____ is a skin disorder characterized by patches of red, scaly, raised areas that usually occurs on elbows and knees.

38. Retin-A is approved only to treat_____ vulgaris but is used off label to diminish wrinkles.

39. _____ is a fungal infection of the oral and/or vaginal mucosa.

40. The _____ is the layer of skin below the epidermis.

41. Aqueous _____ is fluid present in the eye.

42. Actinic _____ is a condition with scaly skin lesions that are pre-cancerous.

43. _____ is an ophthalmic disorder characterized by high internal eye pressure.

44. _____ is the top layer of skin.

45. Contact _____ is an inflammatory reaction produced by contact with an irritating agent.

46. _____ is the most serious form of malignant skin cancer.

47. _____ eczema produces chronic pruritic eruptions.

48. _____ is an abnormal response of the skin or eye to sunlight.

49. _____ is another term for pink eye.

50. If a drug is _____, it will cause birth defects.

51. A _____ is a virally caused epidermal tumor.

52. _____, which stands for sun protection factor, is a rating given to sunscreens.

Matching–Brand and Generic Drug Names

_____ 53. clotrimazole-betamethasone   a. Cutivate

_____ 54. fluticasone   b. Kenalog

_____ 55. latanoprost   c. Lotrisone

_____ 56. triamcinolone   d. Xalatan

_____ 57. tretinoin   e. Bactroban

_____ 58. acyclovir   f. Zovirax

_____ 59. itraconazole   g. Aldara

_____ 60. imiquimod   h. Lamisil

_____ 61. terbinafine   i. Retin-A

_____ 62. mupirocin   j. Sporanox

Matching–Terms and Definitions

_____ 63. beyond use date

_____ 64. candidiasis

_____ 65. eczema

_____ 66. impetigo

_____ 67. phototoxicity

_____ 68. photosensitivity

_____ 69. ringworm

a. A fungal infection (_Candida albicans_) most commonly involving the oral and vaginal mucosa

b. A fungus that infects the horny (scaly) layer of skin or the nails; also called tinea

c. A hot, itchy, red, oozing skin inflammation; also called dermatitis

d. A superficial, highly contagious skin infection; characterized by small red spots that evolve into vesicles, break, become encrusted, and are surrounded by a zone of erythema

e. A property of a chemical that becomes toxic on exposure to light

f. An abnormal response of the skin or eye to sunlight

g. The date after which a drug should not be used once it has been removed from the intact container

Unit
4

Chemotherapy and Miscellaneous Pharmaceutical Products

Recombinant Drugs and Chemotherapy

16

Reading Drug Labels and Medication Orders

1. Mr. Kelly is currently being treated for colon cancer. Mr. Kelly is 47 years old, 70 inches tall, and weighs 215 lbs. He is starting FOLFOX-6 as his new regimen. The regimen details per cycle are as follows:

   Eloxatin 85 mg/m^2 on day 1

   leucovorin 400 mg/m^2 on day 1

   5-fluorouracil bolus 400 mg/m^2 on day 1

   5-fluorouracil continuous infusion 3,000 mg/m^2 over 46 hours on day 1 and day 2

   a. Find a BSA calculator online (your instructor will suggest some website options), and determine Mr. Kelly's BSA using the formula deleveoped by DuBois and DuBois.

   _____

   b. The concentration for the 5-fluorouracil (5-FU) is 50 mg/mL. How many milliliters will the bolus be? Show your calculations.

   _____

   _____

   c. The following three facts about oxaliplatin are important to know:
      - During the FOLFOX-6 regimen, oxaliplatin must be given at the same time as leucovorin.
      - Oxaliplatin is not compatible with any solutions that contain sodium chloride.
      - Oxaliplatin is usually in a concentration of 3 mg/mL to 5 mg/mL.

   Based on these three facts, what would be an appropriate diluent and volume for the leucovorin?

   _____

d. How many vials of Eloxatin will be required for three cycles of therapy? Show your calculations.

_____

_____

e. The calculated dose for the 5-FU continuous infusion is 6,450 mg. If Mr. Kelly is set to receive this medication through an outpatient infusion pump at a rate of 3 mL/hour for the duration of the infusion, how many milliliters must be provided for the course of therapy?

_____

2. Mr. Kelly undergoes three cycles of therapy without improvement. The oncologist decides to add Erbitux to the treatment regimen at a dose of 400 mg/m². The drug label shows the drug to be dispensed.

a. What is Mr. Kelly's resulting dose?

_____

b. How many vials will be required per dose? Show your calculations.

_____

NDC 0000-0000-00

CETUXIMAB

For Intravenous Use

Caution: Federal law prohibits dispensing without prescription

100 mg (2 mg/mL)

50 mL

Storage: Refrigerate at 2° to 8°C (36° to 46°F). Do not freeze or shake.

3. Mrs. Baribeault is currently being treated with ABVD, a regimen with a high incidence of anemia. She has a hemoglobin of 9.6, which is being treated with Epogen with the following instructions.

R̸ Epogen 40,000 units SC once a week

a. How many milliliters of Epogen will be required per dose?

_____

NDC 0000-0000-00

EPOETIN ALFA

10,000 units/mL
2 mL Multidose Vial

Caution: Federal law prohibits dispensing without prescription

b. How many vials of Epogen will be required per dose?

_____

4. Ms. Amik, a survivor of breast cancer, presents the following prescription:

R Nolvadex 20 mg PO daily

    a. How many milligrams will Ms. Amik receive in a month?

    b. The pills in the pharmacy come in a 10 mg strength. How would you write the instructions for the prescription label?

5. Mr. Garza, a patient currently in postrenal transplant, is being started on Zenapax. The order follows. How many milliliters of Zenapax will be used for the product shown in the drug label?

R Zenapax 65 mg IV × 1

> NDC 0000-0000-00
>
> **DACLIZUMAB**
> Sterile Concentrate
> for Injection
>
> 25 mg/5 mL
>
> **1 vial (5 mL)**
> single use
>
> R_x only

6. Ms. Brady gives you the following prescription:

R Lidocaine Viscous 2%, diphenhydramine solution, Maalox, 1:1:1, dispense 6 oz

How many milliliters of each ingredient will be in the product?

7. Mrs. Blanchard is being treated with carboplatin-paclitaxel for ovarian cancer. Her regimen is as follows. She is 65 inches tall and weighs 160 lb.

R Paraplatin AUC = 5

       Taxol 175 mg/m2

    a. Using the calculator at www.globalrph.com/bsa.cgi, what is the patient's BSA?

    b. If the concentration for the Taxol vial is 6 mg/mL, how many milliliters of Taxol will be used per dose? Show your calculations.

    c. The pharmacist calculates the Paraplatin dose to be 500 mg. How many milliliters of Paraplatin must be used if the concentration is 10 mg/mL?

Understanding the Larger Medical Context

8. A patient just received a kidney transplant and is starting on full immunosuppressive therapy. What is immunosupression, and what are some complications of this condition?

_____

_____

_____

_____

9. If you are exposed to an antigen, which cells would provide you with protection from being re-infected eight years from now?

_____

_____

10. What medications are useful in treating a type I hypersensitivity reaction?

_____

_____

11. How are Neupogen and Neulasta alike? How are the two drugs different?

_____

Dispensing and Storing Drugs

12. Which colony-stimulating factor requires a medication guide?

_____

13. Which anti-rejection drugs require a medication guide?

_____

14. Which tyrokinase inhibitors require a medication guide?

_____

15. Which drug used to prevent recurrence of breast cancer requires a medication guide?

_____

Putting Safety First

Does the requested dose match the typical medication dose in the following orders? If not, provide the typical dosage for each medication.

16. Neupogen is incompatible with dextrose and should be mixed with normal saline.

    _____

    _____

17. When using Neulasta, two doses should be given after a cycle of chemotherapy.

    _____

18. Proleukin treatment consists of two seven-day treatment cycles separated by a rest period of 14 days.

    _____

    _____

19. Mylotarg is infused over four hours and is good for one month after reconstitution.

    _____

    _____

20. A daily dosage of Xeloda is administered in one dose.

    _____

    _____

Understanding Concepts

21. "Magic _____" is a combination of lidocaine, diphenhydramine, and a liquid antacid.

22. Chlorambucil and melphalan belong to a group called the _____ mustards.

23. MAB stands for _____.

24. _____ agents are a class of chemotherapy agents that create irreversible cross-links in DNA.

25. _____ alkaloids are used in treatments of various cancers.

26. _____ is a chemo agent that works like a vaccine.

27. _____ is a chemo agent derived from a sponge.

28. When preparing hazardous drugs, the technician should always work in a _____ cabinet.

29. _____ should always be worn when working with hazardous drugs, even when delivering them to the site where they will be infused into the patient.

30. Good _____ hygiene requires washing both before and after dealing with hazardous drugs.

Matching–Drug Names and Drug Groups

_____ 31. abciximab

_____ 32. adalimumab

_____ 33. muromonab-CD3

_____ 34. palivizumab

_____ 35. tositumomab

_____ 36. trastuzumab

_____ 37. azathioprine

_____ 38. tacrolimus

_____ 39. sirolimus

_____ 40. basiliximab

a. Bexxar

b. Herceptin

c. Humira

d. Orthoclone OKT3

e. ReoPro

f. Synagis

g. Prograf

h. Simulect

i. Imuran

j. Rapamune

Matching–Malignancy with Drug

_____ 41. bladder

_____ 42. brain

_____ 43. breast

_____ 44. colorectal

_____ 45. leukemia

_____ 46. lung

_____ 47. lymphoma

_____ 48. melanoma

_____ 49. non-Hodgkins

_____ 50. ovarian

_____ 51. prostate

_____ 52. renal

_____ 53. skin

_____ 54. stomach

a. Alkeran (melphalan)

b. Bexxar (tositumomab)

c. Blenoxane (bleomycin)

d. Casodex (bicalutamide)

e. Cosmegen (dactinomycin)

f. Eloxatan (oxaliplatin)

g. Lysodren (mitotane)

h. Mutamycin (mitomycin)

i. Myleran (busulfan)

j. Platinol (cisplatin)

k. Tarceva (erlotinib)

l. Taxol (paclitaxel)

m. Torisel (timsirolimus)

n. Velcade (bortezomib)

o. Yervoy (iplimumab)

Matching–Terms and Definitions

_____ 55. antirejection drug

_____ 56. cytoprotective agent

_____ 57. extravasation

_____ 58. MAb

_____ 59. recombinant DNA

_____ 60. immunoglobulin (Ig)

_____ 61. replication

_____ 62. plasmid

_____ 63. granulocyte colony-stimulating factor (G-CSF)

_____ 64. resistance

a. A small circular ring of DNA that can insert itself into bacterial genes and can carry genes from one bacterial cell to another

b. Artificial DNA produced in a laboratory by inserting strands of DNA from one organism into that of another organism

c. Lack of responsiveness of cancer cells to chemotherapy

d. The process of copying the DNA of a cell into a new set of DNA molecules to produce a new cell

e. A protein that responds to a specific antigen; also known as an antibody

f. An antibody produced in the laboratory by a culture derived from a single B cell

g. An agent administered to reduce the side effects and toxicity of chemotherapy agents

h. A medication that prevents the body from rejecting foreign solid organ transplants

i. An agent that stimulates the bone marrow to produce specific white cells, such as the granulocytes

i. The escape of IV fluids into the surrounding tissue

Vitamins, OTC Supplements, Antidotes, and Miscellaneous Topics

Reading Drug Labels and Medication Orders

1. You receive the following prescription, and the drug label shown is the product you pick up from the pharmacy shelf:

   ℞   Cipro 500 mg I bid #120

NDC 0000-0000-00
CIPROFLOXACIN
250 mg
100 tablets
R$_x$ only

   a. Is this prescription okay to fill as written?

   _____

   b. Using the medication indicated in the drug label, how many tablets would you dispense to fill this prescription?

   _____

   _____

2. While working in the emergency room pharmacy, you receive a stat order. The physician needs an empiric dose for acute digoxin toxicity.

   a. What products are available for treating digoxin overdose?

   _____

   _____

   b. What is the empiric dose for acute digoxin toxicity?

   _____

Understanding the Larger Medical Context

3. What is the difference between the calcium salts gluconate, chloride, carbonate, and acetate?

_____

_____

_____

_____

_____

_____

_____

4. What are the two types of total parenteral nutrition? How are they different?

_____

_____

_____

_____

_____

_____

_____

5. What regulations exist for nutritional supplements and OTC herbs?

_____

_____

_____

6. What are the steps to treat an emergency MI?

_____

_____

7. What are typical causes of water deficit?

_____

_____

8. Why is tonicity important when preparing IV fluids?

_____

_____

_____

9. What are the main issues surrounding the use of alternative medicine to treat disease?

_____

_____

_____

_____

_____

_____

10. In the event of a biologic attack, what role would pharmacy technicians play?

_____

_____

11. The emergency room physician calls the pharmacy and tells you that the dobutamine solution in the Blue Alert cart has turned a light pink color. The physician wants the solution replaced stat. What do you tell the physician about dobutamine?

_____

_____

_____

_____

_____

Dispensing and Storing Drugs

Are the following medications available over the counter or by prescription?

12. calcium acetate

_____

13. vitamin B$_{12}$ 1000 mcg INJ

_____

14. dong quai

_____

15. activated charcoal

_____

16. vitamin K

_____

17. penicillamine

_____

18. pyridoxine 2 mg

_____

19. vitamin D$_2$

_____

20. calcium gluconate

_____

21. Jevity Plus

_____

Putting Safety First

22. When mixing TPN, which elements have to be separated so they do not precipitate in the bag?

_____

_____

_____

_____

23. What is the purpose of epinephrine in a CODE emergency kit?

_____

_____

_____

_____

24. What are the three types of anthrax? How is anthrax treated?

_____

_____

25. What is ricin? What harm can it cause the human body?

_____

_____

26. What are the fat-soluble vitamins? Why is it important for people to limit the amount of over-the-counter fat-soluble vitamins they ingest?

_____

_____

Understanding Concepts

27. _____ is an alternative supplement used for GI complaints and flatulence.

28. _____ is a medical food brand of L-methylfolate.

29. _____ nitrite is an antidote for cyanide poisoning.

30. Activated _____ is a treatment in the ER for cases of poisoning.

31. St. John's _____ is an alternative supplement for depression.

32. _____ is an antidote for spider bites.

33 _____ is an antidote for scorpion bites.

34. _____ is an enteral nutrition formula administered to diabetic patients.

35. _____ Plus is an enteral nutrition formulation administered to patients with nitrogen needs.

36. _____ is a vitamin that acts as a coenzyme in carbohydrate metabolism.

37. If a script is written for ergocalciferol, it is for vitamin _____.

38. If someone is deficient in vitamin _____, the symptoms are diarrhea, dementia, and dermatitis (the three Ds).

39. _____ is a probiotic used for vaginitis.

40. _____ is an enteral nutrition formula for kidney dialysis patients.

41. _____ is an alternative supplement used for anxiety or psychosis.

42 _____ is a probiotic used for irritable bowel syndrome.

43. _____ acid is vitamin B-9.

44. _____ acid is vitamin C.

45. A drug that counters the effects of a poison is an _____.

46. _____ is a toxin derived from castor beans.

47. _____ is a condition caused by vitamin-D deficiency.

48. When the lipid separates from the parental nutrition solution, this is referred to as _____.

49. Low blood pH is referred to as_____.

50. High blood PH is referred to as _____.

51. Code _____ is an institutional signal that a life-threatening situation is occurring.

Matching–Drug Names and Drug Groups

_____ 52. amiodarone

_____ 53. digoxin immune Fab

_____ 54. epinephrine

_____ 55. lavocoxid

_____ 56. fomepizole

_____ 57. naloxone

_____ 58. phentolamine

_____ 59. potassium

_____ 60. pralidoxime

_____ 61. procainamide

a. Cordarone

b. Digibind

c. Klor Con

d. Narcan

e. Pronestyl

f. Adrenalin

g. Limbrel

h. Regitine

i. Protopam

j. Antizol

Matching–Terms and Definitions

_____ 62. antidote

_____ 63. antivenin

_____ 64. chelating agent

_____ 65. coenzyme

_____ 66. cracking

_____ 67. enteral nutrition

_____ 68. gastric lavage

_____ 69. isotonic solution

_____ 70. parenteral nutrition

_____ 71. pooling

_____ 72. probiotic

_____ 73. tocopherol

_____ 74. tonicity

_____ 75. vitamin

a. A procedure to wash out or irrigate the patient's stomach, commonly known as a stomach pump

b. Feeding a patient by supplying a nutrient solution through a vein

c. A drug that bonds to a metal ion to prevent it from reacting with biological compounds

d. A chemical other than a protein that is needed to assist an enzyme in performing a metabolic function

e. An organic substance that is necessary for the normal metabolic functioning of the body but that the body does not synthesize, so it must be obtained from food

f. Feeding a patient liquid food through a tube that leads to the gastrointestinal system

g. A drug that counters the harmful effects of a poison

h. A solution with the same level of particles, and thus the same tonicity, as body fluids

i. A material used in treatment of poisoning by animal venom

j. The relationship of a solution to the body's own fluids; measured by determining the number of dissolved particles in solution

k. One of the alcohols that constitute vitamin E

l. A product to restore or promote the growth of normal bacterial flora in the body

m. Separation of lipid from a parenteral nutrition solution

n. A time-saving process used when preparing a three-in-one TPN, in which all electrolytes except phosphate are put into a small-volume parenteral bag and then transferred into each batch

Notes

Notes

Notes

Notes